D0898028

CYBERNETICS

IS VOLUME

131

OF THE

Twentieth Century Encyclopedia of Catholicism

UNDER SECTION

XIII

CATHOLICISM AND SCIENCE

IT IS ALSO THE

107TH

VOLUME IN ORDER OF PUBLICATION

Edited by **HENRI DANIEL-ROPS** *of the* *Académie Française*

CYBERNETICS

By NEVILLE MORAY

HAWTHORN BOOKS · PUBLISHERS · *New York*

First Edition, September, 1963

NIHIL OBSTAT

Joannes M. T. Barton, S.T.D., L.S.S.

Censor Deputatus

IMPRIMATUR

Georgius L. Craven

Episcopus Sebastopolis, Vic. Cap.

Westmonasterii, die VI JUNII MCMLXIII

The Nihil obstat and Imprimatur are a declaration that a book or pamphlet is considered to be free from doctrinal or moral error. It is not implied that those who have granted the Nihil obstat and Imprimatur agree with the contents, opinions, or statements expressed.

H-9542

53678

CONTENTS

INTRODUCTION

The history of the relation between the Catholic Church and scientific progress is one of a series of unnecessary troubles. Almost invariably, when a major change in the conceptual framework of some branch of science has occurred, its acceptance by Catholics has been delayed by decades, if not longer. Sooner or later there is an acceptance of the new framework, and an adaptation to the new ways of thought. But, in the meantime, there is almost always a period when a response which bears most of the marks of panic appears. It happened in astronomy, at the time of Galileo; it happened in the last century over the theory of evolution; it happened again over the development of scientific psychology in our own time. In this case the ludicrous situation has been reached where, as far as the present author knows, there are only three Catholics in academic psychology teaching posts in British universities, and four years ago there was only one; and this in a country where the Catholic population is some 10 per cent of nearly 60,000,000 people!

This apparent fear of new concepts in science is not of course so evident in the increasingly large circles of Catholic intellectuals. But at the level of general knowledge it occurs time and time again. The result is that children in the schools are inadequately taught about the new developments, and the Catholic community fails to contribute its quota of workers to the new fields of knowledge and hence fails to play a full part in the society of which we are all members.

It seems to the present author that all the signs point to a more than usual degree of difficulty over Catholic thought adapting itself to the language and concepts of cybernetics, when that discipline begins to make a real impact on our lives and thought.

This book is offered in the hope that it will do something to prevent the withdrawal of our community from the field of cybernetics, and that, on the contrary, it will encourage people to enter research in what, from a philosophical, biological, or engineering standpoint, is one of the most exciting intellectual disciplines of our time.

CHAPTER I

THE ORIGINS OF
CYBERNETICS

Although, as we shall see, there have been devices in existence for many years which in fact embody the principles which lie at the core of cybernetics, the development of the science in a self-conscious way dates only from some twenty years ago. During the Second World War there was a rapid advance in the development of many sorts of weapons, and notable among these was the aeroplane. Bombers and fighters began to fly faster and higher than ever before, and within four years the average speed of attacking aircraft nearly doubled. As always, defensive weapons were developed to match the performance of the attackers, but it became apparent that certain limits in the performance of human beings were resulting in the defence being outperformed by the attackers.

Consider for example the task of the gunlayer, trying to train his weapon on a fast high-flying attacking aircraft. If the shell from the gun is to hit the target, the gun must be pointed ahead of the aircraft, and the shot fired at such a time that when the shell has travelled thousands of feet in one direction it will have followed a course which will bring it into collision with the aircraft which is moving in a different direction and at a different speed. Clearly, to perform such a task a complicated mathematical method must be used, and the results of the calculations translated into movements of the gun. And while the human organism is quite adept at performing this kind of calculation, accuracy alone is not enough: as the speeds of both projectile and plane become faster and faster, by the time that a man has performed the necessary calculation the plane will be past and the opportunity of the gunner gone.

So there began to be developed machines which would perform the task for the man. Machines received information from other machines (such as the radar sets), giving estimates of the height and distance of the attacker from moment to moment; other machines performed the necessary calculations on this information, to work out the speed and direction of the attacker; and yet others fed the results to the controlling mechanisms of the guns and fired them at appropriate instants when they were pointed in appropriate directions. Where before a man had looked, calculated and acted with his eyes, brain and muscles, now the machines received information through their sense organs (the radar scanners), calculated with their nervous systems (the high-speed computers), and acted with the motors and gears (which were their counterpart of muscles) for the execution of their decisions. The *artefact*, the system built synthetically to imitate a human performer, came of age.

In fact these were not the first artefacts. There had been calculating machines of various kinds in existence for many years, though not until the science of electronics was highly developed were their full capabilities revealed in anything like the richness we are now beginning to see.   And there had been many humbler devices—the governor of the steam engine, the thermostat—which, as we shall see, were logically similar to the newer and more complex artefacts. But the close and obvious parallel between the functions which the gunner performed and which the artefact now performs for him, and the division of the artefact's functions into reception, calculation and action, paralleling exactly (from the point of view of their effect on the situation) the reception, calculation and action of the human gunner, serves nicely to underline the inquiry which we are to pursue for the rest of this book.

If a machine can acquire information, can use it to make decisions, can act on these decisions, and can note whether it is successful; and can then, in the light of its mistakes and successes, adapt its behaviour so that it performs better in the future—if this, then what might not a machine be able to do? Where do the limits lie? and are there, or are there not, certain things which distinguish man from the artefacts which could in principle one day exist, not just those which exist already?

These questions are not central to the task which in practice cybernetics carries out; for in many ways it is one of the most practical of the sciences. But as in any science there lie behind the methods and investigations which make up its practice certain theoretical questions which comprise its philosophy. And it is obvious from the nature of cybernetics that its philosophy raises important questions for a man who wishes to understand his own nature.

Cybernetics is the study of the behaviour of systems of all kinds. It is the science of "input" and "output". For as we have seen in the case of the gunlaying problem, what we want from our artefact is that it should behave in the same way as the human operator behaves when doing the same task. But we have at once to make a qualification: we mean by this not necessarily that the way in which it does the task is the same, not that the mechanisms are the same, but that the *behaviour* is the same: when a particular stimulus occurs (a plane in a particular position, at a particular speed, and moving in a particular direction) then the appropriate response occurs (a shell fired at a particular angle, in a particular direction, at a particular speed). We try to design a system, an artefact, in which the relation between its input and its output are the same as in the system we are trying to imitate.

Now if an artefact is to adjust its behaviour with the aim of bringing about some particular state of affairs in the environment, it must find out how things are going, whether its current behaviour is improving things or making them worse, just as a human being would do. And this brings us to one of the central concepts in cybernetics—*feedback*. This property is one which must be shown in some form by any system which produces purposive, adaptive behaviour; behaviour, that is, which sets out to achieve some particular end, and ceases when that end has been reached.

For example, consider the way in which drinking behaviour is controlled in a thirsty animal. We know from physiological evidence that there are some parts of the brain which appear to be sensitive to the concentration of the fluids which make up a large part of the body. When we lose a lot of water (for example on a hot day), the concentration of the body fluids rises, and this activates various mechanisms which cause the organism to seek water. When it finds water it begins to drink, and continues to drink until other sense organs inform the activating centres that enough water has been drunk. Then the action of seeking water and drinking ceases. Information is "fed back" to the brain to control the drinking behaviour. Similarly, a bat which is hunting on the wing sends out short pulses of sound and listens to the echoes which return from the objects near it in the air. When an echo corresponding to prey is heard, the bat alters the path of its flight in the direction of the source of the echo, the next echo gives it more information, and so on. If it is turning quickly it may overshoot, and then suddenly the echoes, instead of coming, perhaps, from its left, now come from its right. So it turns back again. All the time the echoes "feed back" information about the success of the bat's navigation in pursuit of its prey, and help the bat to make the error in its path through the air ever smaller and smaller, until it can seize the prey as it passes.

Finally, as an example of feedback in a purely mechanical system, consider an anti-aircraft rocket which is not controlled from the ground but which "homes" on to its target. There is some device (probably a radar set) which detects a target ahead of the rocket. If the image on the radar screen is off to one side, messages are passed to the steering mechanism and the motors steer the rocket so that the image of the target moves towards the centre of the screen. Probably (as in the case of the bat) the correction will be too great, and the nose of the rocket will overshoot, and another command from the radar set will again turn the rocket so that it tends towards the target. Always the error in direction will be minimized, and the process is called one of control by *negative feedback*, since the feedback information always stops the error from growing greater.

Various other examples of control by feedback will occur to the reader. When driving a car we alter the car's position by turning the steering wheel, and information is fed back to the brain through our eyes as to how successful our adjustment has been. One of the difficulties of a man who goes blind is that up till now he has been used to relying, very largely, on visual information to control his movements about the world. When he loses this he must learn to use auditory and touch feedback instead, and this raises very great problems for him. And similarly, Market Research and Public Opinion Polls are feedback which firms use to control the quality and quantity of their products, so that the discrepancy between their production and the public's willingness to purchase is minimized. The school report at the end of term may be regarded as a means of getting feedback from the educators about what needs to be done to our children to optimize their success in life (although this is perhaps not a very effective control system).

As we saw when introducing the idea of systems which mimic behaviour, there are many things—rockets, bats, car drivers —which appear at first sight very different, but which all have in common the fact that they are self-controlled by means of negative feedback. Indeed, any system which needs to change because of changes in its environment, but which must keep itself within limits ("not too thirsty, but not bloated"; "not in the middle of the road, but not on the pavement"; "no stock-piling, but enough to meet demands") *must* be working by negative feedback. Hence we can add to our knowledge of how to build artefacts which can look after themselves: "they must have negative feedback".

It is for this reason that Norbert Weiner, the brilliant mathematician who may be regarded as the father of cyber-netics, defined his brainchild as "the science of communication and control in the animal and in the machine"; and took the word "cybernetics" from the Greek word $\kappa\nu\beta\epsilon\rho\nu\acute{\eta}\tau\eta\varsigma$, "a steersman". It is a science of control, because we want to try to specify a machine which will give us a particular output whenever a particular input occurs. That is, we want to con-struct systems which *do* things, and to make systems which *do* things we must understand how the parts are to be arranged so as to control one another, and also the environment around the machine, so that the desired output is achieved. And it is a science of communication in two senses. First, as we have seen, control to achieve a particular end must mean that there is communication between the system and the environment. The system must know what is going on around it—whether it is in the region of water if it is thirsty, whether it is in the correct lane when driving, and so on; and so to build such a system we must understand how information can be made to enter it from the world. And secondly, the various parts of the system must communicate with each other within the system: the radar screen must send signals to the rudders and elevators of the rocket, the part of the bat's brain concerned with hearing must send appropriate orders to its wing muscles (to fly and steer).

But there have been several rival definitions, and in some ways it might be more appropriate, at least for our purposes, to call cybernetics "the science of applied logic". This is by analogy with physics. Theoretical physics attempts to analyse and give a theoretical account of the nature of the physical world, and to describe it in the most accurate possible way. Applied physics takes these results and uses them to manipulate the world. Now we shall see later that while we might describe the task of logic as being to give an analysis of what we mean by everyday terms (such as "purpose", "learning", "choice", "perception"), so the task of cybernetics is to examine how this analysis may be used to allow us to simulate these activities in artificial systems which we can construct and which—as we shall also see—can be made to construct themselves.

As a preliminary exercise in how the process works, let us ask whether we could make an artificial system ("artefact") which could show the behaviour observed in any or all of the following group of activities:

Feeding when hungry and stopping when enough has been eaten,
The relation between a learner and a teacher,
The formation of social norms of behaviour,
Running a business,
A political referendum.

We shall only perform a preliminary analysis, aimed at showing that there are certain features which all these phenomena have in common, and that some of these perhaps can be imitated artificially but it will serve as an introduction to the harder work which is to come. It must be understood that when we have reached the end of the next section of the discussion we shall *not* be in a position to say that we can build an artefact to do *any* of the behaviours listed, let alone all of them. But we shall see that they have some things in common of which already in this book we have begun to have an understanding.

Let us start, then, by looking at exactly in what "being hungry and feeding appropriately" consists.

In a human body, the main source of energy to keep the living tissue going is a form of sugar. And there is quite strong evidence that the feeling of hunger arises because the amount of sugar circulating in the body falls below a certain level, and that certain parts of the brain are sensitive to this. These cells then make the organism active and it moves about and will eat things which either it instinctively knows are food or has learnt to be so, until certain other cells sensitive to the arrival of food in the body cause it to stop.

But we could give an even more general account of this process. After all, the point of acquiring and keeping a large amount of sugar in the bloodstream is simply to provide energy. Feeding restores the normal condition of the animal, and overeating which could be dangerous because of the strain placed on the expanded stomach, etc., is prevented by a device which is sensitive to the amount of material which passes into the organism. In general, providing the organism is normal, enough energy-producing material is taken in to restore the organism to the state in which it was before it used up the energy. Hence in the most general terms we may describe feeding behaviour as follows: a system may be said to be doing the same thing as feeding if it pauses from its other behaviour to make up for losses of energy by taking action to absorb energy in a form appropriate to the nature of the system, until the normal state of that system is restored.

It will need to have a part which is sensitive to the loss of energy from inside it, and another which detects the sources of energy in the environment about it, and another which makes it act in the appropriate way to use the latter to offset the former. Now, if for the moment we leave aside the question of whether a non-living system can ever do the same thing as a living organism (we shall come back to this point later on), it is quite clear that we could make an artefact which showed such behaviour. Indeed, if there were an enterprising motor car manufacturer who also owned some garages, he might fit his cars with a device which was sensitive to a beam of light sent out from his garages; and if the petrol was below a certain level in the tank his cars would automatically turn into the next garage of that particular brand and would not start again until petrol had been put it. Such a car would, *in some sense*, be feeding: at the most general level of description ("taking in energy to replace . . ., etc.") it would be doing *exactly* what the organism was doing when it fed. Although of course no one would for a moment suggest that there is no difference between a car and an organism. In practice, if we wanted to make an artefact to show feeding behaviour, we would not build it into a car, but start from scratch, and choose anything we liked, whether petrol, sugar or something else, as its food. Notice that it is at the most general level of description, at the level of a formal analysis of the *properties of the behaviour*, not at the level of the description of the actual *physiology of the organism*, that the two systems, organism and artefact, are similar, and indeed identical. Notice also that both the organism and artefact are using feedback to control their survival and achieve self-preservation: the one if it does not take in energy will die, the other run down and stop.

Turning our attention to the learning-teaching situation, we may do a similar formal analysis. And here it is obvious that the situation is one involving feedback: the teacher gives instructions to the learner, and then tests him to get feedback information as to whether or not the instruction has been received and acted upon. The learner asks questions and gives answers to the teacher so that he in turn may learn by information fed back from the teacher whether he has understood the instruction which he is receiving, and to discover whether he is performing well. The rôle of communication here is rather different from that in the previous case. There it was concerned to restore the system to its initial, optimum, state. Here it is to make the properties of the system (the learner) alter in such a way that its behaviour will be different from before. A definition of learning might go something like this: we say that a person (animal, system) has learnt when behaviour alters as a result of events in his history so that his behaviour in the future shows certain new features which are more appropriate for the relevant situations than the old ways of behaving were.

With such a definition we could certainly construct a system which would show the behaviour. A rather clumsy one might work like this. Imagine a wheeled trolley which had on it a motor, and some bumpers which could reverse the direction of its motion (there used to be a toy car on the market some years ago which did this). We put it into a maze, and it has to "learn" to find its way out. It has a camera with which it takes pictures of the maze as it goes through it, and a device rather like a television camera which can look at and compare the maze with pictures which the device has taken on previous trips through the maze. We finally arrange that if it goes into a blind alley (so that it reaches a point where the only open lane the television camera can find is behind it), then the picture of the junction at which it turned is marked with a special mark to which the television comparison device is sensitive, and sends a signal to turn the wheels one way or the other if it ever matches the photograph with what it now sees.

Such a machine would get badly stuck the first time it went through the maze and would go down a lot of blind alleys. But as it accumulated more and more photographs, each marked with a signal to turn left or right, based on the past runs into the maze, so the machine would get better and better at finding its way through the maze, and eventually would make no mistakes.

Such a machine would in fact be a very clumsy way of producing learning behaviour. But, if we can just forget for a moment that it is a *machine* and concentrate on its *behaviour*, what it *does*, it is showing learning. In this case it gets feedback information from the television camera which informs its "memory" and controls that it has got into a blind alley.

With the last two cases I have tried to show how one could actually construct a machine to show the behaviour in question.

With the remainder of the list of phenomena we set out to investigate I shall not do this; for in the later parts of the book we shall see that there are some rather peculiar things we shall want to say about them. But I want to point out some of the features which they have in common, unlikely though it may seem, with the cases we have already considered.

In the formation of social norms of behaviour we see something like this happen (the following remarks are based on empirical evidence from social science). A group of people comes together for some reason. They discover that they have a certain amount in common. By talking to each other they compare their views on a number of things, and over a period of time we can observe that views come to be more and more held in common by all members of the group. Similarly, although the people may not realize it themselves, their behaviour begins to become increasingly similar too, at least in those aspects which are relevant to the common purpose which the group has. Members who join and who have very deviant attitudes and behaviour tend to change their behaviour more than the others; although if they are too deviant they will be expelled from the group.

Now here again, although this is a long way from either feeding or learning a maze, the systems do have some formal properties in common. For example, it looks as though a process of learning by feedback is in progress. The individual members of the group are altering the behaviours they show by eliminating some (deviant) ones, and acquiring new (conforming) ones, and this must be by a process of observing the effects of their behaviour on the other members of the group, and so altering their own as to reduce the discrepancy between their own repertoire of behaviour and those of the group. If all the members of a set of organisms behave like this then we shall necessarily observe behaviour which we should describe as "formation of behavioural norms". And since we have already shown that we can construct artefacts which both use feedback and show learning behaviour, at least *those* two features of norm formation could be duplicated artificially, although there might be others which could not be so duplicated.

Similarly, when we consider running a business, we can point to certain aspects of the control of manufacture, supply, number of employees, and so on, which have features in common with the processes which we have already discussed. Indeed, this is very like a combination of feeding and learning in some ways. Like feeding, the object of efficient running of a business is at least to prevent the business getting into a state in which its existence is threatened ("bankruptcy", "starvation") by using information about its internal state and the effect of its behaviour on the environment through internal communication and feedback. But also it has the element of trying to change its behaviour (its effect on the environment) so as to improve its own organization ("putting on weight for the winter", "building up a reserve of profits to offset depreciation of machinery"). And so, in a rather obvious way, surprising as it may seem, some of the *formal properties* of running a business, when we analyse them for the most general description, rather than in terms of the day to day actions of actual men in a particular firm, appear to be very similar to a system showing self-preservation and learning.

Finally, there are some very obvious similarities in the "behaviour" in which a political referendum consists, and the adaptive behaviour and self-preservation which we have seen to be a formal similarity of several of the systems which we have been discussing. The object of a referendum is normally to discover whether the electorate is likely to stand for certain measures being implemented. Now through the referendum the government discovers (through a very obvious feedback of information) what the relation between the government and governed is: we might well say that the object of the referendum is to discover whether society is in a stable condition temporarily: or if not, in which direction change must be made ("to what state the system must move") for stability to be restored. The object of a stable society is clearly an example of a system which is showing "self-preservation", for there will be no crises, no need for sudden elections in the middle of the term of office, and the government can be reasonably sure that when an election comes it will be returned to power. And by feedback it can tell what changes are appropriate, try to make them, and by further feedback of information (not merely through the referendum but also through letters from constituents, Gallup polls, and so on), the statesmen learn which changes are the most adaptive (which most readily and most successfully keep society stable).

All this may seem a considerable distance away from a simple account of how we are to try to build machines which imitate or replace human beings or animals. But this lengthy excursion has been taken with an important point in view. It is most important to have clearly in our minds what we mean when we say that we want to build an artefact which will duplicate human behaviour. We might put it this way. It is not —at least in the first instance—that we want to imitate *human* behaviour, but that we want to imitate human *behaviour*. To put it a little differently, we do not want so much to *imitate* or *duplicate* a human behaviour, as to replace it with something which achieves the same end. (It will only be later, when we consider the purely philosophical implications of these ideas, that we shall have to return to the discussion of whether we can imitate *human* behaviour as distinct from human *behaviour*.) We know that we can train a human being to perform a skilled task by having him work beside a man who is already skilled, watch what he does, try to duplicate his actions, try something slightly different if his attempt to copy does not result in the same end product, and so on. If we can make a machine with receptors sensitive to light (photo-electric cells), with touch receptors (strain gauges and proximity switches), and put it to work beside a man; if it then alters switches and dials when he does, and first of all often gets it wrong; but later—through the use of feedback and some built-in criterion for measuring the quality of the product it is making—it shows performance that is increasingly like that of the man, and eventually as good as his, then we shall say that the machine "learnt", has "shown adaptive behaviour", "has been trained by the man". It is not made of flesh, but since the result of its actions for any given situation are the same as those of the man, it seems not unreasonable to say that, in a simple and obvious sense (and leaving aside any metaphysical problem), it is doing the same thing.

We have now reached an important conclusion. Often cybernetics is thought of as the problem of building machines, and that its task is concerned with planning electric circuits and so on. People are inclined to ask, "are not all these machines very worrying? Won't we be able to build a machine to do everything that a man does *when we discover new sorts of gadgets*? How do we know what will happen in a hundred years time?" Or on the other hand, they say, "Don't worry, machines are only made of nuts and bolts; they can't do what living things do. Look at the clumsy robots which people have built. They never work well". And here they are thinking of the sort of robots which are sometimes built, and which by rights should be confined to the pages of science fiction. The robot housemaid is not a thing with arms and legs of metal which can climb stairs and make beds, and clear the things from the table and wash and dry them in the sink. To the cybernetician it is the architect's blueprint for a house where the central heating reduces the need for bedclothes to a minimum, where the layout of a house means that things do not have to be carried up and down stairs if they are heavy, and where the kitchen table is so related to a dishwashing machine that the old-fashioned domestic habits which were such a strain on the housewife are no longer needed. The same behaviours ("running a house", "keeping warm in bed", "keeping the bed tidy", "washing up"), are performed, so that the behaviour of the house and its occupants is the same. But we do not try to build a mechanical man or woman when we try to remove the drudgery from human life; to make machines perform tasks which are drudgery is a waste of the machine, just as to make a human being do them is a waste of a human being. We must concentrate rather on designing systems which perform behaviours that are logically indistinguishable in their end result from the behaviours which we want to replicate.

Even when power units became available, it would have taken many, many decades to make a flying machine if man had tried to duplicate the flapping wing of the bird: to this day no successful ornithopter has been built. Instead, man built a system with the same formal property of "rising into the air and travelling through it"—and today aeroplanes fly at thousands rather than tens of miles an hour.

The flapping wing machine, the ornithopter, is the "machine age" answer to the problem of flight. The aeroplane is the answer which a cyberneticist would suggest.

We see then, that we are concerned with the *logic* of behaviour, with the *formal*, *general* description of behaviour. The question which we ask when we say "can I build an artefact, an artificial system, that will learn?" is not concerned with "have I got enough nuts and bolts? Are the transistors big enough?" (for these questions can be answered by "yes", at least on the basis of future technological development). Rather we mean, "what properties must any system have if it is to show the relation between its input and its output which we call 'learning'? What is it that an animal does which makes us describe it as 'learning', and not just giving a reflex response? *Regardless* of whether we know what a thing is made of, irrespective of whether it is flesh, or wood, or glass, or ceramic, or metal, or plastic, how must its parts be related so that it alters its output adaptively?"

This means that we can now ask questions about any

conceivable artefact, and do not have to wait for the development of new materials by the scientist and technologist. We shall not be concerned with electrical diagrams, but with logical diagrams.

To bring this introductory chapter to a close, we can take a preliminary look at three problems to which we shall return in much greater detail later on: purposive behaviour, self-preservation, and self-reproduction. Each of these is generally considered to be something especially typical of living things.

As to the first, the guided missile which is directed not from the ground, but by radar inside the missile itself has, as we have already seen, many of the characteristics of a purposive system. It behaves as if it were trying to intercept the target. When the target alters course, so does the missile. When the target dives or climbs so does the missile. And turn and twist how it will, the target is relentlessly pursued through the sky by the missile. Remember, we are not suggesting that the missile is in any way "conscious" of what it is doing. But the behaviour it shows is certainly "goal directed", "continues until an end has been achieved", "is purposive".

With regard to self-preservation, we have already suggested how various systems (small groups, governments, businesses), other than individual living animals, can be seen to be behaving in a way which tend to keep them in the state in which they are already. An animal which is feeding itself, drinking, avoiding objects which have hurt it in the past, and so on, is preserving itself. In another phrase, it is trying to keep itself in a state of equilibrium with its environment. If it has to walk about, so that it uses up energy, then it tends to restore itself by acting so that the energy content of its body is restored to an equilibrium value. If it has sweated and so lost water, it takes in enough to offset this loss and to return to equilibrium. To imitate such behaviour in an artefact we simply have to build one which has parts which are sensitive to the critical states which are dangerous to it, and which, whenever one of these is reached, shows purposive behaviour until the variable (energy, temperature, etc., as it might be) is restored to a value which is not in the danger zone. For example, suppose that we made a little toy car, which ran by batteries. We could mount a light-sensitive unit on it, and this would tend to make it run about in the middle of a room, since the middle of a room is usually lighter than the sides or corners. If we arranged it so that when its batteries were low it now sought the darker parts of the room (the light-sensitive switch was turned off when the batteries were low), then it would tend to seek the edges and corners of the room, and would almost inevitably steer itself, sooner or later, to the neighbourhood of an electric plug, where it could recharge its batteries.

Such a device would be merely a toy, but it would show a primitive type of behaviour which could rightly be called "equilibrium seeking" and in some sense "self-preserving", since it would preserve itself from running out of power. On a more elaborate scale we can imagine a big computer which has a temperature-sensitive device which turns it off temporarily if the result of working many hours makes it overheat, and which starts itself up again when it gets cool (our old friend the thermostat again). This is clearly a case of self-preservation: if it did not happen the computer would melt. But there is an important sense in which it can be shown that we can construct an artefact which tends to seek equilibrium conditions which are optimum and which preserve its *status quo*. Ashby has shown that if we have *any* very complex device which is trying to show some particular behaviour, that even if it is damaged or disturbed, it will probably rearrange itself and go on doing what it was doing before. Rather than a matter for surprise that some systems show self-preservation, it is a matter of surprise when they don't! (We shall return to this problem later. For the moment an analogy may help. In a small village, if we dig up one road we may be able to stop someone going from end to end of the village. But in a city, where there are many backstreets, it is almost impossible so to stop someone. He will always be able to find an alternative route. And we shall see later on that the description of the various successive stages of a bit of behaviour can be likened to a plan or map in a very precise sense. If you stop a person, or a thing, from doing something in one way, he will do it in another way. And here the word *way* is quite literally like a way or a path on a map.) Ashby managed to prove that any large system which has a lot of parts richly connected to each other, will tend to show such behaviour.

Thirdly, to imagine a system which reproduces itself is surprisingly easy. Imagine a device like a very large computer, which can collect the various components of which it is made, from a source of supply in the world around it. We give it instructions through a punched tape, just as normally we instruct computers to perform calculations. The tape of instructions reads somewhat as follows.

"Connect part No. 1 to part No. 2. Connect part No. 3 to part No. 4. Connect the two parts you have made", and so on. Thus a new machine will be constructed like the first one. The last three instructions on the tape read like this: "Copy out these instructions and put them in the new machine. Start the new machine up. Cut it loose from yourself."

Clearly, the new one will likewise begin to produce others, and these in their turn will produce yet more. The systems are self-reproducing.

We have now seen something of how cybernetics came into being as a separate discipline, which is neither exactly engineering, nor physics, nor biology, nor psychology; but which has certain features of all these disciplines. We have seen that it is often thought of as the science of machines, and that while in a sense it is true, it can be misleading to call it this if we think of it as implying that it is concerned with the problems of specifying the nuts and bolts which must be used. It is the study not of particular machines, but of machines *in principle*.

So we can ask general questions like, "Can we make an artificial system, an artefact, which can learn?", and not have to wait to see whether we have the right kind of nuts and bolts for the task, but simply turn the question into a slightly different form, and ask: What do we mean when we say a system of any kind "learns"? How must the input and output of such a system be related, and how change in time? How, *in principle*, should we connect up the parts of such a system, supposing we had them and they had the appropriate properties?

And it is for this reason that, in order to say how to make an artefact to perform a particular task, to show a particular behaviour, we first analyse the meaning of the word which we use to describe the behaviour, and then describe how we may duplicate the component parts of the description, that we might well say that *cybernetics is the science of applied logic.*

CHAPTER II

THE LANGUAGE
AND METHODS OF
CYBERNETICS

We have so far made use of two words, "artefact" and "system" when talking about the kinds of things with which cybernetics is concerned. If we are to learn to think about the world in the language of cybernetics, then we must look a little closer at the second of these. For while we have used the word *artefact* to describe an artificial machine designed to imitate some aspect of human or animal behaviour, the word *system* can be used in a much more general way. We might for example define an *artefact* as the physical embodiment of a *system* which we have designed on paper.

In all works about cybernetics this word *system* occurs again and again. We say that we want to design a system which learns, a system which can respond to different patterns, a system that will translate from one language to another, a system that will control the temperature of a room. The advantage of using this word is that we can consider a wide variety of different things which are physically very dissimilar, but are logically the same in terms of what they do. To talk of the particular objects which do the things in which we are interested is apt to puzzle us, for they *look* so different that we are very loth to see the similarities. If, however, we turn the description the other way round, and say, speaking for example of "learning", that *any system which shows changes in behaviour which are adaptive and the result of what has happened to it in the past is showing behaviour that is correctly described by a single name, perhaps "learning"*, then it helps us to concentrate on the similarities between things, rather than on their differences, and this is important for our purpose.

A glance at the sentence which is in italics above will show at once that the way in which we are using the word *system* is rather like the way in which the word *thing* is often used in everyday speech. But we can use the word *system* to cover an even wider range of phenomena in the world than the word *thing* generally covers, and so it is even better for our purpose. *Things* are generally fairly solid and easily identifiable, while even so physically tangible a phenomenon as weather seems slightly unsuited to be called a *thing*, although the word *system* fits it rather well even in everyday language. (The weather forecasters often speak of "a system of low pressure which is developing in the North Atlantic", and they mean all the features which go together to produce a certain set of weather qualities.)

When we think of objects in the world around us, it is fairly obvious that they have a set of attributes, which can be used to describe them. For example, a table has length, breadth, height, position in a room, colour and so on. A table is a fairly stable object and these attributes do not often change, unless I move the table, or paint it. A cat has a set of attributes too, which can be used to describe it, but some of them change rather more. It too has length, breadth, and height, and a position in the room, and a colour or colours. But the position in the room often changes, and if we take a look at the cat during the whole time that it is in existence, many of its other attributes also change. For example, in becoming a cat from a kitten, the odds are that almost *all* of its attributes will change, length, breadth, height, weight, colour, and certainly position.

We can make a kind of map of the natural history of the cat —or for that matter the table, though the idea of the natural history of so inert an object as a table may at first seem odd— by drawing up a *matrix* of its attributes as they occur at successive moments in time. We treat the system "cat" or the system "table" as if we observed it in a series of glimpses at very short intervals. An example of such a map in the case of the cat and of the table is given in Matrix II, 1.

Now let us look for a moment at what this map shows in the case of the cat. It describes, as we read successively the value of each of the attributes of the cat from moment to moment, a cat whose colour and size did not change, but which walked across a room to begin with and finished up by jumping for the last part of its trip. In short, if we make a map, or matrix, in which we describe the values which each of the cat's attributes takes from moment to moment ("Now it is by the door"; "Now six feet from it"; "Now nine feet from it"; "Now eighteen feet from it"), we have described its *behaviour*. And we have described it in a very important way. For if any other system has the same matrix, and the same changes from moment to moment within the matrix, then it will be a system which is indistinguishable from the system which we usually call a "cat". (Since all the attributes have the same values— 14 in. long, black and white, near the door: 14 in. long, black and white, six feet from the door, etc., as a particular cat.)

Now it follows from this that in principle, if only we can describe the behaviour which we want to imitate accurately enough, in the form of a matrix which specifies the behaviour, then we can make a system which does the same thing, providing we make it go through the same changes in *its* matrix in the same order as the system which we are copying. This may sound complicated, but it is just another way of saying what we have already said in the previous chapter. If we can describe exactly what the behaviour we want is like, then we can set about building an artefact which may not look like the original system, but will do the same things.

Think of the original example which we took, that of the change from a humanly controlled anti-aircraft gun to a completely automatic radar controlled unit. The matrix which

Behaviour matrices for a table and a cat (Matrix II, 1)

STATE OF THE SYSTEM

Time	Attributes of Table	Attributes of Cat
t_1 ↓	6 ft from door: 4 ft from window: 5 ft long: 3 ft high: 3 ft wide. Colour—black. ↓	2 ft from door: 10 ft from window: 16 in. long: 8 in. high: 4 in. wide. Colour— ginger. ↓
t_2 ↓	as in t_1 ↓	3 ft from door: 9 ft from window: 16 in. long: 8 in. high: 4 in. wide. Colour— ginger. ↓
t_3 ↓	as in t_2 ↓	4 ft from door: 8 ft from window: 16 in. long: 8 in. high: 4 in. wide. Colour— ginger. ↓
t_4 ↓	as in t_3 ↓	5 ft from door: 7 ft from window: 16 in. long: 8 in. high: 4 in. wide. Colour— ginger. ↓
t_5 ↓	as in t_4 ↓	6 ft from door: 6 ft from window: 16 in. long: 8 in. high: 4 in. wide. Colour— ginger. ↓
t_6 ↓	as in t_5 ↓	10 ft from door: 2 ft from window: 16 in. long: 8 in. high: 4 in. wide. Colour— ginger. ↓
etc.	etc.	etc.

SUCCESSIVE MOMENTS IN TIME

mapped the behaviour of the man who used to do the gun-laying might have looked like this:

Behaviour matrix of gunlaying (Matrix II, 2)

Formal Time	State of System
t_1	Gun pointing north-east at 60° above horizontal.
t_2	Gun pointing east-north-east at 60° above horizontal.
t_3	Gun pointing east at 70° above horizontal.
t_4	Gun pointing east at 75° above horizontal.
t_5	Gun fires while pointing as in t_4.
t_6	Gun is reloaded while pointing as in t_5.
etc.	etc.

And what our automatic gunlaying system must do is to go through the same sequence of changes in each of its attributes as the man showed.

This example brings out another point. There would be some features in a matrix which described a man's behaviour which would not appear in the final matrix describing the system which we expect to duplicate that behaviour. The matrix which described the man could be made extremely complex. If we put in all possible detail we could include the colour of his hair and eyes from moment to moment, what his blood pressure was, what he was wearing, whether he coughed in the middle of the task, and so on. Now most of these attributes, while certainly being necessary to describe the whole behaviour of the man, are not needed to specify the actual task which we are interested in. There are in principle an infinite number of details which could be included. To take an absurd example, we could even put in how far he was from London, or Liverpool, or New York, at each instant. Each of these is a meaningful attribute, and a measurable one. And in a sense each of them *is* really part of the total description which it is possible to make of the man. (And in some cases such attributes might be important, as when a sheriff tells a gang of outlaws, "If I see any of you inside the town limits I shall shoot you". In this case an estimate of the attribute "How far from the sheriff's office" from moment to moment becomes crucial for all concerned, whatever else they may be doing at the same time.) But it seems that something has gone wrong. We do not feel that the colour of a man's hair is really relevant to a description of how he aims a gun, as far as his efficiency as a gunner is concerned. And of course one of the problems involved in specifying the nature of the system which we are trying to analyse and duplicate is to discover the relevant attributes, the ones which are really important.

It is rather as if we had a very large map of a country, and observed on it the movements of a man from one region to another. His movement from one region to another is his behaviour. The map is a rather curious one because as we look more and more closely at it we see ever more and more detail. At one level we see that the man went from Lancashire into Westmorland. We look a bit closer and see that he went along the road from Lancaster to Kendal. We look closer still and see that he went on the left-hand side of that part of the road called "The Prince's Way" at Levens Bridge. Closer still and we see that he touched certain stones of the wall of the house called Levens Hall; and closer still we can say what part of each stone he touched as he passed. And so on.

Now these are all descriptions which together add up to make a complete description of the behaviour known as "travelling from Lancashire to Westmorland along the A.6 road". And we could have gone on to add a list of the traveller's physical characteristics, such as his hair colour, his height from moment to moment (and this would probably vary: he would sit down from time to time for a rest), and other attributes which would specify a particular traveller making this journey. But let us think what would happen if we wanted to make an artefact, a "system" that would copy the behaviour of the "traveller". Which of the attributes we should use would depend upon exactly what we wanted by way of behaviour.

If we simply wanted a system which would go from Preston at one time and to Kendal some time later we need not specify any more than these two names: but we may find that the "traveller" is a train. If we want to make sure that the "traveller" goes by road, then we had better include those attributes which specify closely the places and objects it passes along the way. If we want to make sure that the "traveller" walks, then we had better include those attributes which describe the movements of his legs ("left foot in front of right foot at 2.15; right foot in front of left foot at 2.15 and 2 seconds": and so on.) And, if we want to make sure that the "traveller" looks like a human being, then we shall have to include much more detail.

Although the problem of describing behaviour looks at first sight impossible because we can go on adding more and more attributes, the job is simplified because really all we have to look for are the attributes which are relevant to the question we wish to answer. It is like having a map whose features we can magnify if we need to get extra detail, but which we use with as little detail as possible. In the case of imitating the behaviour of a living animal, the map is really the life history of the organism, and we merely use the detail in that part of the map which is relevant to our purpose.

There remain two points which must be observed. The first is that there is a very obvious rejoinder that might be made by a person sceptical of this method of designing artificial systems. He might say, "You tell me that I have to use only these attributes which are relevant to my purpose. But how do I know which they are? For all I know, if I want to design a system that will catch mice at least as efficiently as a cat, I *should* take account of its colour, the materials of which its skin is made, and the roughness of its tongue. How do I decide whether these are relevant or not?"

There are two ways in which this problem may be solved, and in practice both are usually essential. Firstly, we can sit down and think about the behaviour which we want our system to show. What is its real essence? Can we apply a logical analysis to discover the nature of the task and define it exactly? After all, the mouse-catching behaviour of a cat, as far as its functional effect is concerned from the householder's point of view, is that the mice are prevented either from damaging the food or household goods, or from returning to their holes.

Whether the cat eats them, kills them, scares them away, or makes pets of them is not really important. What is essential is that the map or matrix of the system

Behaviour matrix of system House-with-mice (Matrix II, 3)

Formal Time	State of System
t_1	Mice in holes: no mice in rooms.
↓	↓
t_2	Mice in rooms.
↓	↓
t_3	Mice eating food.
↓	↓
t_4	Mice in rooms but not eating food.
↓	↓
t_5	Mice in holes: no mice in rooms.

should be altered to read:

Behaviour matrix of system House-without-mice (Matrix II, 4)

Formal Time	State of System
t_1	No mice in holes: no mice in rooms.
↓	↓
t_2	No mice in holes: no mice in rooms.
↓	↓
t_3	No mice in holes: no mice in rooms.
↓	↓
etc.	etc.

And of course the essential point about the behaviour is that there should be no mice in it!

Now this may sound very elementary, and indeed as if we

are making much ado about very little. But there is an important point: by observing that the *essential* thing about a cat as a mouse catcher is the disappearance of the state "Mice Present" from the matrix which defines the behaviour, we see that we do not have to try to make an imitation cat, complete with hair, whiskers, and so on. This was realized many years ago, and the result was the mousetrap. But if it all seems rather obvious, think back to another example in Chapter I where men tried for many years to build machines which flapped their wings like a bird in order to solve the problem of flight.

The second way in which we can find out whether we have discovered what the relevant and important attributes are is quite simply by trying out the system we have designed and seeing whether it works. If it does do the task (show the behaviour) as we hoped, then we can conclude that we have found all the important attributes. If it does not do as we hoped, then we alter the combinations of attributes, or add some extra ones, and then try again, and go on until we do reach a combination which works. This is of course making use of feedback to decide when we have reduced the error between what we want to do and what actually happens to an acceptable amount. The reader will remember the discussion we had about feedback as an important element in the intelligent performance of tasks in the first chapter. In a sense we are allowing the system to organize itself with our help; and we shall see that there is a whole class of self-organizing systems with very peculiar properties which are among the most important that we shall discuss.

The second point is one which is of no very great practical importance, but which is interesting from the point of understanding the way in which the language of cybernetics is organized. We mentioned some time back that a table could be described by a matrix of attributes just as an organism can. And indeed we drew up such a matrix. Now as we have been seeing, when we have a matrix which describes the state that each of a system's attributes is in from moment to moment, we have a map of its behaviour. Should we then say, what sounds rather strange, that the matrix which describes the table describes the *behaviour* of the table even though the table is not an organism, and is not alive, and indeed hardly ever changes any of its attributes?

The answer to this is that we should indeed talk of the behaviour of a table. The matrices which we draw up to describe the behaviour of a system show what the system changes into at each moment. We divide up the "life history" of the system into samples which follow each other in time, and each one tells us into what state the system has just changed. Now the sort of things which we think of as being unchanging and permanent in the world, at least over a reasonable length of time —things like rocks, and jewels, and even for most purposes tables—can also be treated as if they are things which change into themselves at each instant.

This is of course the same as saying that you cannot see any change which has taken place from moment to moment, since at each moment the system is just as it was a moment ago. But it is not entirely perverse to look at things in this way. There is a curious satisfaction which comes from the elegance and generality which such a way of looking at the world gives to the theory of cybernetics. For if we are prepared to accept this account, instead of there being two kinds of things in the world, unchanging and changing ones, there is only one kind of thing, of which the apparently permanent one is a special case. The πάντα ῥεῖ of the Greek philosophers returns in a new form and a modern dress. And there is this point to be made. If we look more and more closely at an object (as when we spoke above about making a larger and larger magnification of our "map" of behaviour), we shall find that in fact it is changing. Tiny changes corresponding to wear and tear, minute specks of dust sticking to it, and at the atomic level molecules constantly leaving any object and going into the air around it, or being absorbed from the air—all these constitute changes which are always going on, but are not usually (unless we are atomic physicists, or furniture polishers), among the relevant attributes for describing the systems as we meet them in everyday life. It is not then as stupid as it might seem to describe a system which "does not change" as one which "changes into itself at each moment".

Here we can stop for a moment and see where we have got to in this chapter. We set out to see how cyberneticists use the word "system", and how its meaning was related to words like "thing" and "phenomenon" in ordinary language. And now we can summarize what we want to say about this. The object of cybernetics is to examine the properties of all systems which occur in the Universe as we know it, and where possible and useful, to construct systems which will show the same behaviours as the systems which we observe. *And a system is any set of attributes and the history of the changes of that set of attributes.*

This chapter has been rather rambling in its discussions of various systems, but probably the only way to become familiar with the language of cybernetics is to use it until it becomes familiar in practice. In order to bring out one or two points, which must be clear if we are to understand the framework of ideas with which we are involved, we can look at one or two more examples of systems analysed and defined in the language of sets of attributes and changes.

Let us consider the problem, perhaps a rather unrealistic one, of making an "artificial footballer". It is odd at first to think of a game of football as a "thing", but we can in fact map its "life history" by using a matrix, just as we could map the life histories of organisms or inert objects. Consider a particular man playing a particular game. We can describe his map of behaviour by saying where he is at each instant with respect to the other players and the edges of the field. We should also include a list of his positions with respect to the ball. Then we shall in fact have a rather elaborate and formal description of his play. Some of the combinations of attributes will describe the motion of kicking a ball, and the next few after each of those will describe where he kicked the ball to, and what happened to it and him.

There is one very important point about this system. When we come to identify the relevant attributes for describing our "football player system" many of the attributes are irrelevant. The really important ones are those which describe the relative positions of the man and the ball and the relation between the ball and other men. It does not really matter whether the player is six feet tall, whether or not he runs fast, and so on. Providing no rules are infringed, the important thing is that the ball should show a certain behaviour. It should as far as possible move from near one of the player's own team to near another, and not to a region of the field where any of the opposition are. It should never (if possible) go anywhere near the player's own goalkeeper, but if it does it should go very near him indeed— always near enough for him to be the next one to play it. And whenever possible it should go into that relation with the field and the other team which is described by the attribute "in their goal".

So if we wanted to make an artificial footballer, we should not need to bother about giving him a head, or boots of the right kind, or many of what at first sight are the obvious things. The kind of robot which often figures in stories for schoolboys, which looks like a mechanical man, would probably be a rather inefficient way of making a footballer. What we should do is to concentrate on making a system which when placed in contact with the other attributes of the system which we call "a game of football" would ensure that the ball showed the same behaviour, as nearly as possible, as when the man played for whom the artificial system is substituting. Providing the ball always went from the region where the "artificial footballer" was to near one of his own side or into the opponents' goal then good football behaviour in at least one very important sense would be achieved.

There might be other objections. It is probably not practically possible to design such a system, although theoretically it is a comparatively simple device. And people would not enjoy watching it to the extent that they would enjoy watching real players. And lastly, the rules would probably be interpreted to exclude any non-human participants—but that is a matter for the Football Association and not for the cyberneticist.

We have now seen some of the ways in which the language of cybernetics is built up. We have talked about describing any phenomenon which occurs in the Universe in terms of a set of attributes which it possesses, and how each of these attributes changes with time. Many cyberneticists use a special branch of mathematics called "Set theory" in order to simplify their thinking about a collection of attributes, and often symbolic logic is used in conjunction with this, in order to display the relation between different parts of a concept more clearly. But in the first instance we can use ordinary language, as we have tried to do in this chapter. We have also discussed the problem of selecting the relevant attributes which we need for any particular problem from the infinitely large set of attributes which actually exist. Often the word *variable* is used in books of cybernetics where we have so far used *attribute*; and in the rest of the book these words are used indifferently. Finally we have noticed how we can find out what the important properties of any system are. We can analyse the behaviour into components which we can see logically embody the real functional definition of the behaviour in which we are interested. Or we can make a guess as to what they probably are, and then try to imitate the system, and improve our new system by using information which is fed back from its errors to rearrange the variables (attributes) which describe its behaviour. Finally, as we saw in the first chapter, we have seen that many systems which seem to be extremely different at first sight are in fact rather similar, at least for some purposes: a mousetrap and a cat are *identical*, the same thing *exactly*, as far as the behaviour of the system "Mice in house" is concerned; although they are not identical as far as the system "Reproduction of cat species" is concerned. Once again this serves to underline that as cyberneticists we must think in terms of the most general possible features of the problems which we try to solve.

CHAPTER III

HOW TO MAKE A MACHINE WHICH CAN COUNT

This chapter is not essential to the development of our discussion of how cybernetics looks at the world. But it may be useful to see how in practice and in some detail we might use the methods which we have been looking at in order to solve a particular problem. Since counting often seems a very human bit of behaviour, let us consider a machine which would count. To be more precise, let us consider how to make a system which will distinguish the number "4" from any other number, and make a specific response whenever "4" occurs: it will have the concept of "fourness".

Suppose that we are faced with the following very practical problem. Sometimes when people are trapped in a mine by a fall of rock they try to attract attention by tapping the rock. But clearly if there is a very big rock fall they will not be able to make the sound carry through the rock. The first thing that can be done is to make an amplifier with which to listen for tapping noises, but if there is a lot of other noise going on as well, such as pumps, and rock crumbling, then the tapping may be drowned by the other noises.

However, we can improve things a little by thinking as follows. If the tapping is very faint, we shall sometimes hear it during a lull in the other noises, but not very often, and the trouble is that we shall keep on saying, "Well, I *think* I heard something, but I'm not quite sure". The more often that we manage to hear it the more certain we become. And if the trapped men always tap a particular pattern which is even slightly complicated, then in the end we may decide that there is someone tapping, because noises which occur by accident, natural noises, do not very often come in regular patterns. So we ought to tell people who work in mines, "if you are trapped, always tap a regular pattern". And a fairly simple one to use would be the sign for "V" in morse code, dot-dot-dot-dash. This could be tapped out "tap, tap, tap, tap—pause—tap, tap, tap, tap—pause—" and so on, with the taps coming at about one each second.

If we could keep a record of all the noise which was going on, we should find that over a long time it would add up to an overall average of noise, and that the regularity of the pattern of four taps would stand out as the one complicated repeated pattern in an otherwise random, miscellaneous collection of noises. Unfortunately, our brains are not very good at doing this kind of task when the situations are very noisy and very irregular. How could we devise a system which would be an improvement on the human performance?

We have told the trapped men that they are to tap out groups of four taps at one second intervals, pause for a while, and then start again. Now we do not know how long they will pause between each group of four taps, and people are not very good at tapping at exactly once per second, although if they tap somewhat slower than their heart rate they are not likely to be too much in error, and even just guessing what one a second is like they probably will not be more than an eighth of a second out. So what we want is a system which will be sensitive to "fourness" in signals which reach it, but only if the "fourness" comes at one per second, more or less, and regardless of how long there is between groups of four.

Let us draw up a matrix describing the behaviour which we want the system to show. We start from a moment when the first noise comes, and count in tenths of a second, and we give the system an output which is a light which flashes whenever it receives a louder than usual noise at the correct moment, which is anywhere between $\frac{9}{10}$ second and $1\frac{1}{10}$ second after the previous tap, to allow for human inaccuracy in tapping. We make the system so that after a noise is received, it becomes insensitive until a second is up, and again just after that, and so on for four times. We must then arrange that if it has only received a noise at three of these sensitive times, it will not make a signal, and that if after it has received four it receives another, it will not make a signal to tell us that there have been some noises. The matrix of its behaviour, must, in short, look like this:

Behaviour matrix of counting artefact (Matrix III, I)

Formal time	Real Time	State number	State of System
t_1	0	1	Sensitive to louder than normal sound: move to State 2 if such a sound comes.
t_2	0·0–0·9 sec.	2	Insensitive.
t_3	0·9–1·1 sec.	3	Sensitive.
t_4	1·1–1·9 sec.	4	Insensitive.
t_5	1·9–2·1 sec.	5	Sensitive.
t_6	2·1–2·9 sec.	6	Insensitive.
t_7	2·9–3·1 sec.	7	Sensitive.
t_8	3·2 sec.	8	Sends signal to observer to indicate whether a louder-than-usual sound has been received at each sensitive period.
t_9	3·2–3·9 sec.	9	Insensitive.
t_{10}	3·9–4·1 sec.	10	Sensitive.
t_{11}	4·2 sec.	11	Cancels the signal from *State 8* if another signal arrives at *State 10*.
Stop	Stop	—	Stop

A system described by such a matrix will in fact do the task that we want. It will only give an output to us when it receives four noises each a bit louder than the background and about one second apart. We could say that such a system has the concept of the number "4", since it can tell four from any other number, and give a specific response to it.

There remains another feature which we must include. The system we have described will only count the first four noises one second apart which it receives. After that we have guaranteed by our matrix of its behaviour that it will be insensitive to any more noises which arrive. But of course what we want it to do is to recognize a "fourness", and then be ready to start again when the trapped men begin to tap a second series of four taps, and so on. For, as we mentioned above, it is very unlikely that a natural noise will repeat a fairly steady pattern of four noises at one second intervals again and again, although it might do it once or twice.

We can include this feature of the behaviour by arranging that the system goes back to its initial state after about six seconds. (It must run at least that long to make sure that there is not a fifth tap. But if the men are pausing for a moment before beginning again, it must be ready to start again shortly after that.) So the matrix of the behaviour we want to reproduce must in the end look like this:

Behaviour Matrix of counting artefact (Matrix III, 2)

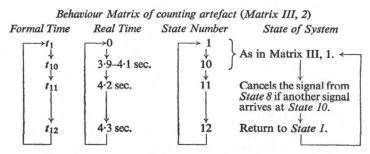

Formal Time	Real Time	State Number	State of System
→t_1	→0	→ 1	} As in Matrix III, 1. ←
t_{10}	3·9–4·1 sec.	10	
t_{11}	4·2 sec.	11	Cancels the signal from *State 8* if another signal arrives at *State 10*.
t_{12}	4·3 sec.	12	Return to *State 1*.

Lastly, of course, we have to make an artefact which will pass through a set of changes in respect of its attributes which is the same as those described in the last matrix, although it can be made of any material we like. Perhaps it is worth while, since many readers probably know a little about electronics, to discuss briefly how we might physically embody this artefact. For those who are not interested in this, but only in the logical questions, the next few pages can be omitted, and they can go at once to Chapter IV. But it is important to realize that in order to show that we can make a machine which can respond to "fourness", we do not have to make it actually in physical terms. To design it logically on paper is enough. We are interested only in logical, not in physical, limitations on our methods and skill. Leonardo da Vinci invented a helicopter which would have flown if only he had had an adequate engine to provide him with the power to drive it. He had shown by his design on paper that it was logically possible for man to fly. The fact that it was not until the beginning of this century that engines with an adequate power/weight ratio could be built was immaterial. Similarly, we shall not be worried if we do not yet have electronic components, or plastics, or metals, with the properties which we require in order to build the physical artefacts corresponding to our behaviour matrices: we have shown that it is possible in principle to make a system to show certain behaviour when we have constructed the relevant matrix, not when we have tightened up the last bolt.

To make our artefact to detect "fourness", we can proceed in detail as follows.

We pick up the noises which are going on with a microphone, and so convert the sound into electrical impulses. The louder the sound the bigger are the electrical impulses. We feed the impulses from the microphone through a circuit which has a resistance in it so that only unusually loud sounds produce big enough impulses to pass through. Beyond this we have the following rather complex set of components. It is possible to make a special kind of transistor, which requires a particular number of impulses to make it work. One kind will pass on an impulse every time that one impulse reaches it. Another kind

will only pass on an impulse if two impulses arrive simul-
taneously. Our artefact has one of the first kind, and several of
the second kind of transistors.

When an unusually loud sound manages to reach the first
transistor in the form of a pulse of electricity, that transistor
passes the pulse on to the next transistor. But this next one is
the kind which needs two impulses to make it fire. Now we
arrange things so that when the first one fires, the microphone
is switched from it to the second transistor. Also, we arrange
electronically that this second transistor, which needs two
pulses to make it fire, gets one of them passed on from the first
transistor after a delay of about a second.

Now the second transistor needs two pulses to make it fire.
One of these it gets from the first transistor about a second after
the latter fires. But this will not make the second one fire in
its turn unless it also gets an impulse from the microphone,
which is now connected to it, and through which an impulse
will in fact arrive if someone taps at that moment. So that if
the second transistor does in fact emit a pulse in its turn, we
know that at least two "taps" have come at the right interval.

Now if we have two more of this kind of transistor arranged
in the same way it is clear that we can detect a third, and then
a fourth "tap", if they come. And lastly we have an extra one
to defect a fifth "tap". If an electrical impulse emerges from the
fourth transistor, we arrange it to work a counter, or switch on
a light. But we make it do this only after a delay of a second,
and if the fifth one fires in that time, we make it switch No. 4
off. Lastly, we arrange that the very first one does one other
thing, and that is start a clock-device which makes the microphone go back to the first transistor after six or seven seconds
regardless of what happens.

This system will do everything we want of it. It will start
counting whenever an extra loud noise arrives at the first
transistor. It will then automatically detect any input which
occurs at or about one second intervals after that, and if there

is a group of four, but neither more or less, it will indicate that to watchers. It will not mind if the groups of four taps come at very irregular intervals, providing that they are more or less one second apart. And by making it work a counter it can add up the number of occasions on which "fourness", that rather rare characteristic of natural noises, occurs.

It will do what we wanted, count "fourness" and nothing else, because a description of its behaviour is a matrix which is identical with the matrix we originally drew up. If a human being listens to a series of noises and counts that there are four of them, the matrix of his *behaviour* is exactly the same, although not of course, the mechanisms by which he does it.

CHAPTER IV

THE NATURAL WORLD AND ITS DESCRIPTION IN CYBERNETICS

Far and away the most systematic and reliable collection of facts which we have about the natural world of which we are a part is that which science has gathered together. On the whole scientists understand that the conventions within which they work and the methods that they use have much in common throughout the different sciences, whether physical, biological, or behavioural. The rules for testing whether a theory is correct, or for repeating an observation or experiment are held in common among scientists, and out of the great mass of experimenting and observing which has gone on down the centuries have emerged the scientific laws, generalizations about the nature of things which allow us to predict, control, and understand the world in which we live.

Possibly the most general way in which a scientific law can be stated is that it says something like, "If so and so, then such and such". If we apply heat to water, then it will boil. If we apply a stimulus to a certain area in the brain, then the person will feel a tingling sensation in his hand. If we mix aluminium and caustic soda, the aluminium will be dissolved and hydrogen given off. It is hard to think of any scientific laws which cannot be converted into this "If . . . then" form.

As a result of this, we see that the scientific laws offer us predictions about events in the future, based on past evidence. In fact, each scientific law describes a small behaviour matrix, the behaviour matrix of that system which is the part of natural phenomena with which the particular law is concerned. For example, "At time T the kettle has a temperature of 20°C and has 1 pint of water in it. At time T' the kettle has a temperature of 100°C and has 1 pint of water in it. At time T'' the kettle has a temperature of 100°C and $\frac{1}{2}$ pint of water in it" is the description of a kettle which heats up, boils, and then goes on boiling until half of the water has boiled away. (Or else someone has poured some water out during the short interval between our observations at the last two times.) The scientific law predicting the effect of heating on the kettle with water is of the form, "If the attributes of the system (kettle+water+heat) have certain values at this moment; then at a future time T' they will have the following values . . .".

Now other sorts of knowledge about the world look as if they can be put into a similar form. The development of a friendship, for example, might be described by a behaviour matrix, which at a rather coarse level of description would go something like this. At first the two people had never met (state A). Then they met (state B). They became better informed about each other (state C), and so on. Then if we give the list of the states through which the system "Two people who at first were strangers" went, with the order in which it went from state to state, and the times at which it happened then we have a description of the development of a friendship, in terms of the behaviour which is observable by someone not involved, and who does not know anything about the two people other than his observations. (He does not know whether they are really only pretending to be friendly from some ulterior motive, for example.) In practice each state would have to be described in much greater detail. This is what social psychologists try to do.

Another example of a system which can be described by a behaviour matrix is the history of my education. I went to school X at time T (state A). Then at time T' I went to school Y (state B). Then to University Z at time T'' (state C) and so on. Here the system whose behaviour matrix we are describing is "Human being educated". While as a final example, the list of the kings and queens of England with their dates is the behaviour matrix of the system "England under a monarchic form of government".

By this time, the reader will probably have got over the shock of finding such unlikely groups of things (systems) as a boiling kettle, a developing friendship, a boy being educated, and the history of a country being lumped together to show that they can be represented by some very general kind of description which underlines the formal qualities which all the systems share. But now, for a change, we can retrace our steps and look at the differences.

We start by summarizing a sample of each of the systems in terms of their respective behaviour matrices,

Now one of the charms of these maps of a system's life history which we have been drawing, and which we have been calling matrices of behaviour, is that we can predict future states of the matrix from the state we find it in. For as we construct the matrix we have said at each step, either, "we observe that when the system shows the behaviour in which I am interested, it goes through the following states"; or "if I were to have a system which went through the following states, then it would duplicate the behaviour I am interested in". ("I observe that the gunner swings the gun so that it points in a direction 15° ahead of the aircraft and raises the barrel 78° above the horizontal when the plane is flying at 350 miles per hour and is approaching from the south-east. He then points it 5° ahead of the aircraft and straight up when it is not quite overhead, and then 30° ahead of the aircraft and 60° above the horizon when it is flying away from him to the

Behaviour matrices of four natural systems (Matrix IV, 1)

Formal Time	State number	Real Time	System: Heating Kettle	Real Time	System: Developing Friendship	Real Time	System: Schooling History	Real Time	System: Monarchic Britain
t_1	1	11.00 a.m.	Temp. = 25°C Water = 2 pints	Jan.	Have not met	0–5 years	at home	1066–1087	William I
t_2	2	11.10	Temp. = 50°C Water = 2 pints	Feb.	Have met once : spend 1 hr./week together	5–10 years	primary school	1087–1100	William II
t_3	3	11.20	Temp. = 75°C Water = 2 pints	Mar.	Have met 3 times. Spend 4 hr./week together	10–15 years	primary and Grammar school	1100–1135	Henry I
t_4	4	11.30	Temp. = 100°C Water = 2 pints	April	Have met 10 times. Spend 1 hr. per day together	15–20 years	Grammar school & University	1135–1154	Stephen
t_5	5	11.40	Temp. = 100°C Water = 1½ pints	May	Have met 60 times. Spend 2 hr. per day together	20–25 years	University then no school	1154–1189	Henry II
t_6	6	11.50	Temp. = 100°C Water = 1 pint	June	Have met 100 times. Spend 2 hr. per day together	25–30 NO SUCH STATE IN THIS SYSTEM		1189–1199	Richard I
etc.	etc.	etc.	etc.	etc.	etc.	NO MORE ENTRIES IN THIS SYSTEM		etc.	etc.

south-west.") We can also say, "If my artefact makes the gun move through the same set of positions in the same order when the plane moves in the same way then it will achieve the same result as the gunner". And if in fact the result is that the plane is destroyed, so that we decide that this matrix of behaviour is a good one, then whenever the first part of it appears, we can predict the later states from it.

But can we?

It is true that all else being equal there is only a single path of behaviour which we can follow through the matrix. But aircraft do not always fly in a straight line, and if the plane changed course just after it had passed overhead, and the gunner or artefact swung the gun to follow it, then our prediction based on past experience would be at fault. A kettle does in fact usually boil when it is put on a sufficiently strong source of heat. But even here it is conceivable (quite apart from any esoteric considerations to do with Maxwell's Demon and the laws of thermodynamics) that our prediction might go wrong if the room in which the kettle was situated happened to be unusually cold. It is generally true that we can predict the next king or queen from the present one, for the system's behaviour (the set of states of attributes to which it can go next) is governed by the laws of succession. But here there are, after all, occasional invasions and revolutions and wars. And the development of a friendship is even harder to predict, for one can imagine two different groups of people doing almost identical things in the same order (being described by matrices of behaviour which are identical), and yet one group will end up firm friends and the other may not. One may take "an irrational dislike" to the other.

The more one compares the various systems for which we have drawn matrices so far, the more one begins to feel that there is something which has been overlooked. There does not seem much objection to the matrix for a kettle which is heating up. One feels that if the value of its present set of attributes is known, then there is a virtual certainty about where it will go next. With the system of Rulers of the Country we feel a little less sure. The laws of succession *ought* to enable us to say with certainty what state (which ruler) the system will show next. But we feel that perhaps there is room for phrasing it a little more loosely. We know perhaps that the king has two sons, and that while one is older, and so should succeed to the throne, he is a bit feeble minded, and the younger one is actually stronger and better liked by the people. Hence we might feel that if we drew up the behaviour matrix for this point in history we should really put in two states to which the system could go, and perhaps add that we think that it is more probable, but not certain, that it will go to one (the elder son) than the other (the younger son).

It is in fact far more common to find systems for which the latter is an accurate description than the former. That is, when we get down to looking at the world in detail, and try to draw up accurate behaviour matrices, we find it is comparatively rarely that they are what is called "single valued". That is, it is rare that there is only *one* new state to which a natural system may go next. Far more often we find that there are several. And the most accurate way we can have of drawing up our map of behaviour is to indicate at each point how probable each of the alternative routes is which the system may take next. A very nice (and at the time of writing quite realistic) example is shown by considering the possible educational history of an imaginary child from an upper middle-class family.

The actual values for relative chances of going to the different kinds of schools are not accurate, but are simply illustrative. In such a system, we can tell the next state which it will pass into within certain probabilities, but not exactly. And in general there are very many systems in the world which are of this kind rather than exactly predictable.

It is important to notice that this looseness of prediction we can make is nothing to do with the fact that we are dealing with the history of a human being, and that humans have "free will". Much later on we shall return to the question of analysing specifically human acts (*actus humani*) in terms of cybernetics. And there I shall argue that contrary to what is usually thought to be the case, free acts are in principle *more*, not less, predictable, than determined ones. For the moment, notice that we do in fact predict the free behaviour of people we know well almost constantly. Every time we say "Oh yes, he is a trustworthy person", we are not merely saying something about his past, but also predicting his future, free, behaviour. In the case of our behaviour matrices, we are not concerned at all with *why* the system goes from one state to the next: it is sufficient to know the paths which behaviour takes through the

Behaviour matrix showing various probabilities of paths through educational history (Matrix IV, 2)

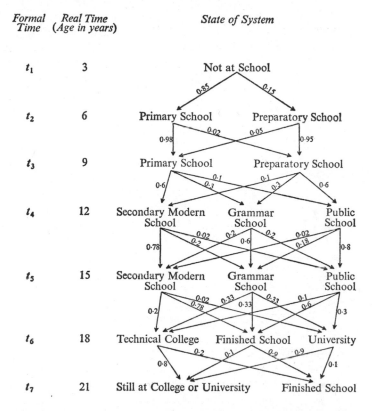

The numbers represent the relative probabilities of the pathways.   Thus 0·6 means six chances in ten; 0·02 means two chances in one hundred; and so on.

maps we have drawn, without knowing whether or not the paths are chosen by one kind of mechanism or another, by a conscious decision or the throw of dice. A matrix of free behaviour would not have any obvious differences from the matrix of determined behaviour except in the names of some of the attributes. We could draw a map of free behaviour in the same way that we can draw the map of behaviour of the radar-controlled gun.

In regard to this matter of predictability, it is convenient to distinguish three main groups of systems in the world. Firstly, there are systems like the kettle where we can predict almost exactly the next state of the system from the last one. Secondly, there are systems like the gun where we can say that if the system is in a certain state now it will go to one of several possible states next, and can give the relative chances of it going to each of them. Finally, there is a kind of system which we have not yet mentioned, but which is far and away the most interesting and important from our point of view, namely those systems which alter their nature from moment to moment, so that a matrix which is correct for describing their behaviour at one moment is inadequate at the next. Such systems typically show "learning", and most living organisms come into this category.

We can call the first kind a *state-determined* system, for the state in which it is at this moment completely determines the state into which it will go at the next moment. *State-determined* systems are completely and exactly predictable.

The second kind of systems have been given the name of a mathematician who first discussed certain problems in probability theory which are closely related to them. This is a pity in some ways, for it would be easier to remember if they were called, say, probability-determined systems; in fact they are called *Markov systems*. And although they can often be *completely* predictable, they are not *exactly* predictable. For the state such a system is in at the present limits the states to which it can go not exactly, but to a small set within which it can go to one of several possibilities each with a certain probability.

The last kind of system, the one we have not yet discussed,

is called a *self-organizing system*, for it changes its properties so that the matrix which is the map of its natural history keeps on having to be altered from moment to moment. And since all we can study (by the rules of the game) are its be- haviours—what happens to the output from the system when we alter its input—and cannot look inside it, all we see is the probability of going from one state to another altering from moment to moment. And since we are still doing the same things to it, but the results of these, the responses or outputs we get from it, are changing, we conclude that its internal organization must be altering. Hence the name of self-organizing. These systems are neither completely nor exactly predictable.

Now despite the fact that we generally think of the natural world as being fully determined (usually in the sense that we do not think that stones or even elephants have free will), there are actually very few systems which are truly state-determined. The kettle approaches being a system of this kind, and so does a new car (although an old one which is rather worn is prob- ably more like a Markov system). Atoms, in so far as we can observe their behaviour, are not state-determined, because our observations alter them (the "Uncertainty principle") and are better described as Markov systems. And all living organisms, from the humble amoeba upwards, are Markov, not state- determined systems. Probably the nearest system to a real natural state-determined system which man has made is a satellite travelling in free space, although even then there are small perturbations in its orbit caused by cosmic dust, the impact of the occasional meteorite, and so on.

This latter example serves to draw our attention to one feature of these classifications. A system may be two of them at once. Earlier we saw that by enlarging the scale of our map of the behaviour of a system, we could notice more and more detail. And a system which is state-determined at one level of description may be Markovian at another. For example, if a man habitually drives to work along a road where there are two houses one hundred yards apart, on a straight stretch of road, he may very well be regarded as a state-determined system as far as the path his car takes is concerned. If we assume that there are no accidents, punctures, etc., then it is certain that after he has passed the first house he will pass the second. Viewed at this level, the behaviour map (first house at time T—second house at time T') is unique and predictable. But if we were to look at the path taken by the car in great detail, we would find that it was better described as a Markov system, for on one occasion it might go along the road one yard from the kerb, on another occasion one and a half yards from the kerb, on another occasion it might swerve to avoid a cat, and so on.

This duality of description is seen in many cases. The fact that the cultural patterns of a society are described with great accuracy by statistical counts does not mean that the individual's behaviour is necessarily state-determined or even Markovian. When Gilbert's soldier pondered on the mysteries of the Markovian dispensation of providence whereby "Every little girl and boy that's born into the world alive, is either a little Liberal or else a little Conservative", this did not preclude (though no doubt many Government supporters wish it did!) the voters actually being self-organizing systems which are free to some degree to decide which political party they belong to. It is, in fact, the tendency of pollsters to regard the system "People Who Vote" as only Markovian which causes such surprise when the system's self-organizing properties come to the fore in a "landslide" election.

Another example comes from the realm of atomic physics. Radio-active substances are both state-determined and Markovian. They are state-determined in that we can predict with exactness that after a certain length of time (the "half-life" of the element in question) half of the atoms present will have undergone a radioactive transformation into another sort of atom. But it is a Markovian system in that we cannot say which atoms are the ones which will undergo radio-active disintegration: as far as we know there is an equal chance for every atom, but only half of them in fact so decay.

We shall pay no further attention to the truly state-determined system, for it is of little interest as far as an analysis of the behaviour of human and other animals is concerned. Reflex responses like the blinking of the eye at the rapid approach of an object, or the narrowing of the pupil in response to bright light, or the sharp reflex raising of the leg when the tendon at the knee is tapped are as near as we ever come to finding a truly state-determined response in humans, and even these can be modified with training by conditioned reflex technique. People sometimes tend to talk as if instinctive behaviour were state-determined, all given to the animal as a set of fixed behaviour patterns at birth; but there is abundant evidence to suggest that even the most rigid instinctive pattern of behaviour can be modified by the repeated application of a stimulus (causing habituation and the disappearance of the response) or by learning during the animal's lifetime, and there is little doubt that for most purposes of analysing and trying to duplicate behaviour systems we may take it that however "determined", in the philosopher's sense of being without free choice, animals or anything else may be, they are virtually never state-determined in the sense in which the cyberneticist uses that word.

Almost all of the systems which comprise the world of living organisms and its features, then, are Markovian. The route taken by a car, the progress of an election, the number of cars produced by a factory, the rate at which the population of the world increases, the railways from the point of view of the time-table—all these, even where they are meant to be rigidly predictable (as for example the railways), are really best described as Markovian systems. And with respect to the behaviour of organisms as individuals, this is even truer. We know that hungry animals will approach food, but even so we cannot say on any particular occasion that a particular animal will for certain approach it, for it may also be thirsty, or seeking a mate, or frightened, and any one or more of these additional factors may influence its behaviour; so that we can only say that it is very probable that if we know the animal is hungry (but not anything else about it), then we can safely predict that it will approach the food. The young puppy which we are training will come when we call on one occasion, but the next time will not come, because a new and interesting smell has caught its attention. And even the most sober and well-mannered human may occasionally "have a fling" and produce most unusual behaviour. In all these cases the systems are not completely predictable; although we may be able to say which possibilities are open to the system (organism), and how probable each of the alternatives is, we cannot predict the outcome uniquely— only as a more or less probable event.

This unpredictability is made even more prominent in systems which learn, and which have self-organizing properties. For when we have drawn up the matrix which describes the possible behaviour pattern open to the system at one time, even if we are completely accurate, some event may lead to its changing its properties. We have no knowledge (by definition) of what has happened inside the organism, only about its overt behaviour, and so we can only discover that the change has occurred when our predictions go wrong. This property is shown to a greater or lesser degree by almost every living system however simple, although it is only in the animals with well-developed nervous systems that it becomes of outstanding importance. And it is certainly the most important type of system to duplicate from the point of view of developing arte-facts to take over tasks from humans.

In conclusion, it should be noticed that this unpredictability has nothing whatever to do with any metaphysical distinctions between "free" and "determined" actions in the sense in which philosophers are interested. From the point of view of empirical predictability, the outcome of a throw of a dice or the outcome of the spin of a roulette wheel are certainly unpredictable (except as one of a number of equiprobable alternatives, and hence a Markov system); but they are if anything *less* predictable than a man's giving money to a charitable cause, or keeping a promise, or choosing to perform some virtuous act or to refrain from a vicious one. (And each of these latter implies a set of alternatives, and hence may be regarded as the matrix of behaviour available to a Markov system.) The predictability with which we are concerned in these cybernetic analyses of behaviour are simply empirically observed relations between inputs and outputs of a given system, between stimuli and responses in an organism, between a repeated offer to a man and the pattern of his acceptance. Providing the same result does not always follow the same stimulus, then the system is to some degree unpredictable, and hence is a Markov system. Whether this unpredictability is derived from an element of randomness, or from an element of rational decision, is a matter for further consideration. Here we are concerned with it simply as a set of possible different outcomes arising from a single input to a system whose inner construction we cannot see or know about.

CHAPTER V

THE BEHAVIOUR OF
LIVING ORGANISMS

The aim of the previous chapters has been threefold. In the first place we have had to study some of the vocabulary which if not exclusively used by cybernetics has at least certain rather special uses in that science. For example, we have met terms like "feedback", and "system", and "behaviour matrix" and seen where they fit into the description of the world from a cybernetic standpoint. Next, we have used this language until (it is hoped) some of its strangeness has worn off and we have begun to feel at home with it. Thirdly, we have seen how by talking in the very general terms which cybernetics uses, it is possible to point out similarities in the logical description of various events in the world which otherwise would seem quite dissimilar. Also we have seen that if a system can be constructed where the logical description which we give of its behaviour is the same as that of some system which we can observe already existing in the natural world, then we can say that the two systems are doing the same thing in some rather general, but at the same time very accurate sense.

Let us now turn our attention to the particular analysis of those systems which we call living organisms, and in particular of that system which we call "man". We shall not start from any metaphysical viewpoint in this analysis. We shall not begin by saying that man is a spiritual being at least in part of his nature, and that therefore any system which is avowedly behaviouristic cannot give a full account of his natural history (or supernatural history). After all, we spend our lives observing the behaviour of men in the world around us. Indeed it is on the basis of this ability both to observe men around us and also to be aware that we are doing things ourselves that we come to the conclusion that men are special in any way. In the end, when we claim that men as such have a partly spiritual nature, what we must mean is that we observe that they do some rather peculiar things which we do not observe other creatures doing, and that we therefore conclude that they are in some sense different from other creatures. Our criteria for telling that we are dealing with a man are always, in the last analysis, behavioural. We go by what he does, by what he says about his experiences, and so on. Man is unique in the animal kingdom in having the kind of language that he has, and in being able as a result to tell other men about his experiences; but it is through their linguistic *behaviour* that we come to know about the experiences of other men. We cannot observe anything in another man except his behaviour. And any decision that we may come to about his materialism or his spirituality must be the result of observing his *behaviour*. Even in the case of oneself one cannot have any direct experience of oneself as a partly spiritual creature. The most we can be aware of is that we do things, that we have experiences. *Cogito ergo sum* is misleading if we think that we can observe our "self". What we are aware of is *ourself* thinking, acting, and experiencing: we cannot observe our *self*.

It is worth while labouring this point. As Aquinas observed (*Summa Theologica*, Ia, qu. 87), I cannot have a direct experience of my own soul. The *cogito* does not lead to that. What I can be aware of is that I act as an agent, and that I have experiences. But it is only when we begin to analyse exactly what it is that I am aware of doing, and how and why I do these things, that we can come to a decision about whether a materialistic or a spiritual metaphysic is needed to give an adequate account of the nature of man. The line which Descartes followed from the *cogito*, leading to the question of who is the subject of the verb, and in the end to a position of rank psychophysical parallelism as a solution to the body-mind problem, is based on a logical fallacy. This fallacy has been attacked by many recent writers, but it seems to have a strangely vigorous life among contemporary Christian thinkers. One of the more recent attacks is that of Geach, in his book *Mental Acts*, to which anyone interested may turn.

The importance of the argument is this. Even if I *think* that I can be aware of something non-physical in my own acts or experiences (and I would suggest that such a so-called experience is certainly an illusion or mistake) the most that I could conclude is that one person, namely myself, has reason to think that there is something non-physical about his nature, *unless I use behavioural criteria to decide about other people.* Parodoxical though it may seem, my decision, if it turns out to be warranted, about the spirituality of others, is based on behavioural criteria. For I can only observe others to see either what they do or what they say. And observing what they say is just as much observing behaviour (verbal behaviour) as is observing where they put their feet, how they move their hands, and when they sit down or rise. If I want to make a metaphysical claim to the effect that a purely materialistic account of human nature is not sufficient to exhaust the subject matter "man", then I can only do it by saying something to this effect: there are some things which human beings do that suggest that a description of them purely in spatio-temporal terms is inadequate. But I can only say this if I have observed their *behaviour* in the first place, and perhaps if I have asked the question "Could I make a system which would behave in this way?", and to my surprise received the answer "no".

A preamble to the examination of human and animal behaviour of this length is probably necessary. For unfortunately the history of the word "Behaviourism" and the phrase "A science of behaviour" is such that the claim that we can only study behaviour is often taken as an unavoidable denial of the Christian account of human nature. When Watson invented the name "Behaviourism" for his science, the implications which he drew from it were certainly such as to justify that comment. But nowadays, while there are very few psychologists of note who would deny that they are behaviourists, the metaphysical questions are seen to be separate, philosophical questions, which arise out of the interpretation of the data which psychology provides, and are not obviously and easily soluble in either direction.

Consequently, it is very fitting that we should analyse the behaviour of the system which we call man. For in every aspect of our everyday lives it is the behaviour of other men and women which calls forth from us our own behaviour. We live in a world of behaviour, and the scientific, objective account of the world of humans must be made in terms of publicly observable events: and as far as organisms are concerned, this means that we describe their world in terms of their behaviour.

Cybernetics is perhaps *the* General Science. For as we have seen, it provides a language and a way of systematizing observations about the world which has a peculiar generality. By the use of matrices, and of other systems of measurement and classification which can be derived from them, but which we shall not be concerned with here, we can apparently always map out the way in which the attributes of any system change with time, and this map we have called the "behaviour of the system". Cybernetics is of extraordinary generality because we can use any of the languages which belong to the different sciences to write out our matrices, and so we can adapt the cybernetic analysis to any of the sciences we choose. There is something odd about describing the growth of a plant merely in terms of the position and momentum of sub-atomic particles: we feel that it should be done in terms of the number of leaves, and the length of the stem, rather than at the level of the atoms which make up the leaves and the stem. That is, we feel that the language of botany is more appropriate to describing the growth of plants than the language of physics. And similarly, that often the meeting of two animals and their interaction, the dancing, the fighting, or the mating, is better described in such terms than in terms of the impulses sent along certain nerves to certain muscle groups.

We feel, in short, that there is a language of physics, and a language of botany, a language of ethology, and a language of physiology. And we feel that there are certain problems in looking at the world and analysing it scientifically which require the use of one or other of these languages more appropriately than another. The method of description which we have been using in this book seems almost to cut across the distinction between such languages. But whereas what the logical positivists were looking for when they searched for the "Unified Science" was a way of translating the terms of all the other languages into the terms of physics, here what we do is to allow the sciences to retain their own languages, but provide a generalized way of manipulating the languages which is logically identical for all, and which therefore serves to bring out similarities, identities indeed, which would otherwise remain unobserved.

Consequently, when we turn our attention to what is *usually* called behaviour, namely the natural histories of living systems, we can ask the following two questions.

"Is there anything special about the language which we need to build up the behaviour matrices of living systems which is unlike the matrices which we can construct in the other scientific languages?" And "Is there any limit to the extent to which we can use such matrices to build systems (as we built the machine that would count 'fourness'), which will behave like living organisms, although they are artefacts?".

In short, to what extent can we build artefacts which will behave like men?

The kind of events which have been traditionally assigned to the realm of living organisms, and above all humans, are those such as "perception", "learning", "purposive action" (teleological behaviour), "thinking", "concept formation", "choice", and other such. Likewise, during the last hundred years, though not, as we shall see, earlier on, the capacity for self-reproduction, and lately evolution, have come to be thought of as the distinguishing marks of living systems. In what sense, if at all, can we ascribe such events to the history of artefacts? And indeed, as a preliminary question, we might ask why it is that we ever ascribe them to organisms other than man.

It does in fact seem quite natural to us to say that a dog "sees", "hears", and so on. That is, we are prepared to say that a dog has various kinds of experiences which are, to a considerable degree, the same kind of experiences that we have when we "see", "hear", and in general perceive. It seems probable that we differ from dogs in the importance which the various sensory modalities have in our lives. As Quoodle, the terrier in Chesterton's *The Flying Inn* remarked, "They haven't got no noses, the fallen sons of Eve"; while on the other hand our vision is certainly very much better than that of the average dog. But since we cannot ask a dog what it perceives, or what its perceptions are like, why do we say that it can perceive? Worms respond to a sudden bright light which falls on them by a withdrawal of the front part of the body, but in this case we do not quite so readily ascribe perceptions to the animal. Rather than saying that a worm "sees" a light in such a situation, we find that people who experiment on such animals rather speak of them "responding" to a light. Similarly there are plants which respond to stimulation. *Mimosa pudica*, "the Sensitive Plant", folds its leaves, its twigs, and its branches if it is tapped with increasing force on some part of its foliage. The Venus Fly Trap goes even further, and having caught flies which land upon it with the sticky surface of its leaves it then closes its leaves up and folds the fly inside, where it is digested by juices which the plant secretes. In these cases we do speak of the plants "feeling" the blow, or the fly which lands. But we should not, I think, speak of them as "perceiving" the stimulus.

The way in which we decide the use of words which in humans correspond to mental functions, the perception words, is not in fact at all simple. We seem to have arrived at a convention that we do not speak of an animal "seeing" something if it merely responds to light. It must also have some structure which is at least loosely comparable to an eye. (Zoologists generally refer to the light-sensitive organs in the worm as, "eye-spots" to distinguish them from eyes.) Also, we seem reluctant to ascribe mental events (or rather, perceptual words) to those organisms, such as plants, which do not have a nervous system. But why do we ascribe such events to animals other than man? We cannot ever have direct knowledge of the nature of their perceptual experiences. For that matter, although we can ask other men whether they have seen or heard something, and if so what it looked or sounded like, we normally do not bother with this kind of questioning in everyday life, but accept quite other kinds of evidence for their seeing something, or hearing something. If we are approaching a set of traffic lights, we do not ask the driver of another car whether he has perceived the lights change to red. We know from his behaviour that he has, when we see his car slow down as it approaches the lights. This is because we know that during the time when a man is learning to drive he is asked such questions as "Do you see that the lights are red?" and when he says "Yes", he is taught that he must stop.

In this last case we know that there is a connection between the behaviour and the perception because we have arranged that it shall be so, since we can discuss with a human being what his perceptions are at any given moment. But with regard to the other, non-language using organisms, the situation is rather different, and two conventions seem to be adopted. With respect to plants and lower animals, we are not prepared to say that they have perceptions because they are too dissimilar physically. They respond to light but they do not have eyes. They respond to touch but (in the case of the plant) they do not have anything corresponding to the nervous system. The organs of touch which man has are anatomically related to those which even the worm has, and certainly they are similar to those of the higher animals. And the nature of nerve cells changes astonishingly little in the course of the evolutionary series. But the organs of touch are so dissimilar in the case of the plants, and the absence of a nervous system is so striking, that we are not prepared to use the same words for the higher animals on the one hand and plants on the other. Similarly in the case of a worm's "vision", the structures which are involved in the visual process are so dissimilar to those in the higher animals, both with respect to the sense organs and to the arrangement of the nervous system, that we do not feel justified in using quite the same language to describe the events in its natural history. But it is important to realize that this is largely a matter of a convention. The similarity between the structures of the nervous systems of worms and the animals nearest to them higher up the evolutionary series is considerable, and we are not worried by using the same language for these two groups. Similarly, if we look at species separated by small steps we do not find an obvious break: it is only with regard to the extremes that we feel unhappy about using the same words ("see", "perceive", and so on).

But why do we ever say of an animal that cannot talk that it "sees a light" rather than that it simply "responds to a light"? There seems no reason to doubt that animals such as dogs and monkeys do have visual experiences; we are prepared to accept the idea even that they dream, which is an activity where even in the case of men we have to ask a person whether or not he has been dreaming. Why?

It seems probable that the use of these words is correct, and that the reason that we use them is because of the similarity of the behavioural evidence in the case of man and other animals. Very often a man does something, such as stopping his car, or turning a switch, or making some kind of response which suggests that he has seen a light. If a night-watchman goes around a building moving light switches from one position to another, and thus turning off the lights, we can conclude from his behaviour that he has seen the lights and is turning them off. We can, if we have need, check on this by asking him whether or not he has seen a light and he will tell us that he did see a light and that was why he pressed the switch to turn it out.

Now in the case of an animal that does not use language in the way we do, an animal, that is, to which we cannot put questions about its perceptions, we are prepared to say that it has had the same experience providing that there is the same kind of relation between the stimulus and the behaviour as we see in humans. We may imagine an experiment in which a dog has been trained to press a button to turn a light off whenever it comes on. We know that if we had trained a man to do this (as is the case when we give a night-watchman his instructions to turn off any lights he may find on, although here of course we are not conditioning him, but merely instructing him), then if a light came on and he pressed the button, we would conclude that he had seen the light. Further, we could check the correctness of our assumption by asking him to report on his experience. That is, we could check our deductions from his non-verbal behaviour by making use of his verbal behaviour. (Note that it is nothing to do with his having a "mind": both these classes of events, the pressing a switch and the answer to our question, are behaviour.) In the case of the animal we have no verbal behaviour to appeal to to see whether our deduction from non-verbal behaviour is correct. But because the creature has eyes, and a similar kind of nervous system to ours, with nerve cells which have the same properties, and because above all the behaviour is related to the stimulus in the same way, therefore we conclude that the same thing has happened: an organism has "seen a light", or "perceived a light".

Notice that we can talk about this question without any sort of worry whether animals have minds, or any such difficult and puzzling problems. Here we simply say that the animal behaves as if it were seeing a light. There is no other question we can ask. To say, "It may behave as if it is seeing a light, but how do we know that it is really *seeing* a light?" would probably mean something to the effect of "How do I know that it is having the kind of experience I have when I see a light?" And this is a question which there is no way, in principle, to answer, so it cannot even be asked. All we can say is, we will say that an animal perceives a light when it reacts to it in such a way that, if it were a human, we could ask it "did you perceive a light?" and expect the answer "yes".

It is for this reason that we are prepared to say that animals dream, which is at first sight a much harder problem to decide. Anyone who has kept a cat or dog for any length of time has seen them, while asleep, make movements as if running, and make noises (whining, barking) as if they were hunting for something. We know that if a human makes corresponding noises (talks in his sleep, cries out) or moves about as if doing something, and we wake him and ask if he was dreaming he usually says that he was. In this case too, therefore, we extrapolate from a case where we can use verbal reports about mental experiences to check the non-verbal evidence for their occurrence, to the case (in non-human animals) where there is only the non-verbal behaviour. And there can be few people who seriously doubt that animals dream from time to time.

We see, then, that where we have an animal which is not a human animal, an animal which does not use language in the way and of the sort that humans use, that we decide what is happening to it, what events are occurring in its perceptual life, by what it *does*, how it *behaves*. On the basis of this kind of evidence we conclude what its experiences are—that it sees, hears, feels; in short that it perceives things in the world around it. If we are challenged by someone who wants to be clear what we mean *exactly*, the ultimate reply which we have to give must be, "The animal behaves *as if* it were having the same sort of experience that humans report verbally in the same situation." But normally we do not bother with this circumlocution, for our definition of what counts as an animal perceiving something is the non-verbal behaviour it produces. What we *mean* by an animal seeing something is that it behaves as if it saw it. There is nothing else that we can find out about the situation.

It should be clear by now how we are going to treat the problem of whether or not artefacts can "see", "hear", in short "perceive". If we say of a system which is made from protein, fats, carbohydrates, and so on, that it shall be said to perceive something when it behaves as if it had perceived that thing (which is what we do with animals which are systems made of proteins, fats, carbohydrates, and so); then we could say this of *any* system. The radar system which we discussed in the early part of this book, which fed information to a gun so that it was able to shoot down an aircraft, a guided missile which alters its course so as to offset the evasive action of its target, and other similar devices all behave as if they were sensing the presence of an object in the world. A better example, perhaps, is the *Machina Speculatrix* which Dr Grey Walter has designed. This is a mechanical toy, driven by electricity, which has a light-sensitive device on it which is linked to the wheel in such a way that the machine tends to approach any light which it encounters as it wanders about. If the light is too bright it will not go right up to it but will circle around it. The wheel of the machine is also connected to the motors but in such a way that when it is touched it inhibits the response to light. Such a machine will show remarkably "animal-like" behaviour. It will approach a light until it bumps into it, whereupon it will withdraw a little. If it is also fitted with a light on itself, it will alternatively approach and withdraw from its reflection in a mirror, moving about and turning round the while, and if two such machines are put into one another's presence, a sort of "playing" occurs, for each is attracted to the other by the light, but upon approaching too close they bump, whereupon the approach response is inhibited, and they withdraw. Because of the way in which they are constructed they never perform exactly the same movement twice, although their overall behaviour pattern is the same, namely that they "play" with one another, on subsequent occasions.

Now of such machines there is every inducement to say that they are behaving as if they saw one another, or as if they saw the light. But at the same time we feel that there is something wrong, and that perhaps it would be better to say simply that they respond to one another. Why do we feel this? It is probably because we know in this case that they are not alive. And we have a great resistance to saying that non-living things "see", or "perceive". Now while this resistance is quite correct, for verbs about mental events are meant, in our language, to refer to living systems, it is important to notice two things. Firstly, it is only in our world that we can be so certain that things made of glass and metal do not deserve to be described as "seeing" or "perceiving". It is quite possible to imagine that when men travel to other planets, they may find one where the landscape is covered with objects which move about responding to stimuli, reproducing, etc., but which are not made of the biological materials of which terrestrial animals are made. The biochemical reactions by which the animals and plants on our planet obtain their energy are not the only conceivable reactions which would suffice to produce "animals", although "life" on such a planet would be very different from that which we know. If we discovered a race of creatures made from quite different physical materials, but which were not being manufactured by anyone but simply breeding, then we should probably

say that they did in fact, see, hear, and so on, depending only
on what kinds of physical signals they responded to, and
not bothering about the fact that they were not made from
protein, fats, and carbohydrates. We must be clear, in short,
about *why* we feel that there is a difference between living and
non-living things. Suppose that Grey Walter's *Machina
Speculatrix* were dressed up in fur, and felt warm to the touch,
and had little feet instead of wheels, and a person were confronted by a pair of them playing—would he doubt, if he did
not know beforehand that the "animals" were manufactured,
that they "saw" and "felt" one another, on the basis of how
they behaved? And if he were prepared to say that they did
perceive one another *before* he knew that they were manufactured, why should he change his opinion just because he
later knew more about their past history? Would it not be
more legitimate to say that they, although artefacts, behaved
"as if they perceived one another"? The second thing to be
borne in mind is one to which we shall return later: it is in
fact logically possible to make a living system from non-
living components.

Our conclusion, then, with respect to perception, is that just
as we are prepared to say of animals that they "see", "hear",
"feel", and so on because they behave as if they did; so we can
certainly construct artefacts which behave as if they can "see",
"hear", "feel", and so on. The reasoning could be expressed in
another way more in line with the kind of things we were saying
in earlier chapters: if the system goes through a behaviour
matrix which has the same behavioural states in the same order,
then we describe it as having done the same thing. What
materials it is made from is not, so far as we have seen, relevant.
(We shall see later that there may be limits to this idea.)

There are several classes of behaviour which are shown by
animals which may conveniently be discussed here. One of the
things which is frequently offered as an example of a capacity
which is only within the range of humans, and not of other

animals, is the formation of concepts and the knowledge of universals. We have to be careful here as to precisely what we mean by "have a knowledge of". Geach has discussed the question of our criteria for an organism having a concept, and he comes down in favour of an analysis in which we may say at the least that a man has a concept if he behaves appropriately. There may be other things which we mean, but it means at least this. He shows that he has the concept of "yellowness" if he can bring us yellow things when we ask for them rather than other coloured things; and he can use the word yellow correctly in his conversation.

In the first sense, that of being able to respond appropriately by non-verbal behaviour, it is clear that animals do have concepts. We may even leave aside such apparently innate capacities as the ability to recognize members of the same species, and certain innate capacities for response to particular shapes and colours as such, which are present in certain animals and might be taken to indicate that the animal in question has an "innate concept of dog-ness", for example. There is ample experimental evidence for concept formation now forthcoming from the laboratories of comparative and experimental psychologists. We feel perhaps that innate responses, such as the tendency for young gulls to peck at coloured spots of a certain shape and size, merit the title of "inborn response" rather than "concept of yellow spots"; and that by rights the having of a concept should be something that is acquired rather than born in one. It seems most properly used in cases where a response which was made to many different things comes to be made only to all the members of a particular class of things.

In this sense the experiments on shape-discrimination which are commonly performed in the course of the analysis of brain mechanisms of animals may be regarded as experiments in concept formation. It is possible to train an animal to respond to, say, triangles as such, regardless of whether they are large or small, acute or obtuse, white or black. Such a performance comes very close to allowing a justifiable claim that the animal is responding to the concept, the universal, of "triangularity" as such, and not to the particular triangles. This is not to claim that the animal has a conscious knowledge of triangularity; not to claim that it, as it were, says to itself, "Ah! a triangle!" whenever the experimenter presents one in a training trial. But that the behaviour is such as to make us conclude that the animal is responding to the universal "triangularity" and not to particular triangles.

A more abstract concept appears to be within the capacity of birds of several species. If such a bird is presented with a series of cards on which there are, say, five spots, it can learn to respond to these cards and ignore others with different numbers of spots. The spots on different cards are different in size, in colour, in shape, in position, having only in common that there are neither more nor less than five, whenever the bird is rewarded. It is difficult to see why we should not say that the bird has the concept of "fiveness". In a different type of experiment the birds can be taught to count sequentially at least to seven. And there is some evidence that birds which have been trained on, say, the spatially arranged five dots, will have their performance on the sequential task improved by such training. In such a case it seems clear that up to a point the animals have number concepts.

An even more complex kind of concept formation is that involving fairly complex *relations* in the response. These problems are among the hardest of all for animals to solve, but when the experimental conditions are optimal they can be solved by several species. Monkeys for example can be trained to pick objects on the basis of "oddity". On successive trials the animal is presented with, say, two squares and a triangle, then two circles and a square, then two diamonds and a triangle, and so on. In each case the animal has to pick the one which is the odd man out, although the way in which it differs is different from trial to trial. Under intensive training, not merely is this problem solved but further elaborations of similar situations can be devised. It is possible to train an animal so that when confronted with a large number of assorted objects, it will pick out all the red ones if it is shown a triangle, and pick out all the blue ones if it is shown a circle.

In these elaborate problems involving the perception and response to relations as such, rather than to particular cases of a relation, it seems quite legitimate to talk of the animal having certain concepts. Once again, it should be emphasized that this does *not* mean that the monkey is able to reflect on what it is doing, or is able to say to itself, "Ah, yes—triangle: that means all red objects". To do the latter an animal would have to have the kind of language which we possess, and no such language is found among animals, even though rudimentary symbolic communication is found in various degrees of sophistication. Simply, it means that the animal behaves as if, as a system, it has the concept in this sense: that faced with a series of problems in which the answer is only obtainable by using a universal concept and not a particular case, those problems are solved by the animal. It behaves, if you like, "as if" it had the concept.

It is equally clear that this kind of behaviour can be built into artefacts. We have already seen in a previous chapter a case of a machine which has the concept of "fourness" as distinct from any other number, when a sequential counting situation occurs. The artefact which was described was fairly limited, for the counting had to be done at a particular rate. But it is not impossible in principle, and given a much larger and more complex system, to deal with counts presented at any speed so that its behaviour would match that of a human being performing the same task. (Both of them would be baffled by certain patterns, for example where the spacing of the counts was such that it was not clear whether a particular one was the last of one group or the first of the next. But the artefact would perform at least as well as a man in such a situation, and it might be possible for it to show more rational strategies in dealing with such a complex situation.) Many workers have discussed the problem of designing artefacts which will show shape discrimination properties, or in general extract the invariant properties when presented with a series of patterns which differ in all except one or two features, whether the patterns are spatial or temporal. One or two such artefacts have actually been constructed, and within the limits of the tasks for which they were designed work quite well, although they are all too small to show the richness of human concept formation in this field. Qualitatively, though not quantitatively, they match the animals. Oddity does not seem to have been specifically dealt with, but there is no difficulty in principle. An artefact which is to recognize all triangles, say, and reject other shapes, must detect which properties of a triangle remain constant when it is made larger, smaller, acute, obtuse, and so on. It must, in short, detect invariants. To solve any oddity problem, these invariants in turn must be classified, and what is invariant about *them* detected. (In the oddity problem it is that only one of them is present singly: there is always more than one example of any of the others: two cases of "triangularity" and one of "circularity"; or two of "squareness" and one of "triangularity".) In principle this is comparatively simple; although, again, an artefact would need to be rather large to do it. This is of course no objection.

It is possible, then, to match all the performances of animals which we have been discussing by the performances of artefacts, at least from the point of view of their behaviour. And if we are prepared to say of the animals, "they perceive", "they form (at least rudimentary) concepts", then we should be prepared to say the same thing of the artefacts, for they show the same behaviour. Once again, the fact that they are at present made of metal, glass, ceramics, and so on must not be allowed to intrude. We could design them with organic components, or we could think of a planet where "animals" were not made of the materials of which they are made here. Or, we can just ask ourselves, suppose someone showed us the records of the experimental sessions, or actually disguised the machine to look like an animal, could we tell the living system from the artefactual system? For *it behaves as if* it were doing what animals do, and we have no way of posing questions about what it is *really* doing, if only we could ask it. Such an idea is meaningless.

In the introduction to the paragraphs about concept formation, we remarked that one aspect which seemed important was the learning, the acquisition, of the concept. We will now turn our attention to the description of the learning, and its modelling with artificial systems. We could, and so far in practice generally do, design pattern recognizers so that they do not have to learn, but have a set range of patterns which they can recognize. They do not have to organize their own responses: the invariants are classified for them, and they do not have to discover them. But the more interesting classes of artefacts, and the ones which in the future development of the applications of cybernetics to everyday life will have an increasingly important rôle, are those which are not programmed in advance, but which learn for themselves, starting with only a very general sort of organization. These are the learning, or self-organizing systems.

The definition of learning is notoriously difficult. We might say that if an animal has a range of possible responses which are observed when a particular stimulus occurs, and those which are rewarding to the animal are retained while the unrewarding ones disappear from the response repertoire, then the animal has learnt. In some cases the role of "reward" is difficult to analyse. There are certain cases in which animals appear to learn in situations where it is not at all apparent that any reward occurs. And of course there is always the point that the responses of animals can be changed—although not so efficiently as by reward—by means of punishment. It might be better therefore simply to define learning in terms of what responses we observe, without considering whether they need be either rewarding or, as they are occasionally, maladaptive. We may then define learning as follows. Initially when we present a particular stimulus to an animal it may give one of several responses to it, and which one occurs seems to be either a matter of chance or of some previous habit. As a result of training, one response, which was previously not the most frequent one, now becomes almost the only one which is given. This change in the probability of getting a response we call "learning"; and when an animal changes its behaviour in this way we say that it has learnt.

Now we can describe this kind of behaviour, and the way in which changes occur, in terms of the behaviour matrix of the organism in question, and to do so is illuminating as an introduction to the properties of self-organizing machines. Let us consider an untrained, naïve animal which we are going to use in an experiment. Initially when we flash a light at the animal, several responses are all equally likely to occur: let us suppose that the dog will either sit down, walk towards the light, or run away. It does these things an equal proportion of the time. We can represent them in a matrix like this:

Behaviour matrix of untrained dog in response to light (Matrix V, 1)

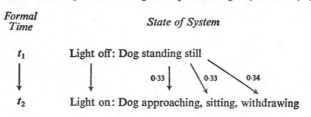

| Formal Time | State of System |

t_1 Light off: Dog standing still

t_2 Light on: Dog approaching, sitting, withdrawing

Now let us suppose that we train it always to sit down, so that instead of having three paths along which its behaviour may go when a light is flashed, it only has one. It is true that we have apparently changed a Markov process into a state-determined one: but we have in fact done far more. For it is not merely the actual response that we have altered: we are bound radically to have changed a large segment of the dog's behaviour. Before, on at least some of the occasions, the dog might go on to do things like sniffing the light (after it had approached it), or leaving the room altogether (when it ran away). But in future, if our training is successful, not merely is the approach or the running away prevented, but *all behaviours which follow on from these*, since they have been removed from the matrix, and hence cannot be reached by the animal, at least directly. It may be that there is another pathway which the behaviour may take —for example light flash—animal sits—animal patted— animal goes to sleep—animal wakes to find light has gone— animal leaves room. But any behaviour which followed directly from leaving the room when the light was flashed, without any interval for sleep, will now be lost from the animal's behaviour reportoire. For example, if there was something which would have caused a habit to form in the animal which only occurred just after the light flashed, then that habit will now never be formed. If an animal learns to go to sleep immediately after breakfast, this may prevent him from biting postmen, and from biting people who carry sacks (and hence look like postmen as far as he is concerned), and so on.

We could formalize the animal's behaviour before and after learning with two matrices, as follows, where again, the letters of the alphabet each refer to a different thing which the animal does, or could do.

After training, not merely are the responses B, C, and D no longer seen, but also the behaviours M, Q, X. And any habits involving these latter will be lost. And L, though it is still done, is done only after something which was not necessary before. (It could occur after C and Q, but now must go through the acts following A.)

The importance of these matrices is very great, and it is worth while emphasizing this point. When we are dealing with

Behaviour matrix of untrained dog in response to light (*Matrix V, 2*)

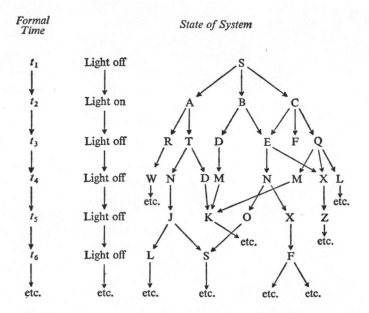

In this matrix each letter stands for some behaviour which is open to the dog at that point, but which can be reached only if it has just done something from which an arrow leads to the point we are examining. Thus if S is *sitting*, J is *jumping*, and O is *rolling on the ground*; then we see that for this dog, if he once moves from a sitting position at time t_1, he will not sit again unless he has just either jumped or rolled, since only from J and O do arrows lead to S (see time t_5 and t_6). Whatever X stands for (perhaps *eating*), the dog will not sit after doing it, for no arrow leads from X to S in any part of the matrix.

a self-organizing system, and we alter one of its properties, so that a part of its behaviour matrix is altered, we shall often, indeed usually, find that we have altered many other properties of its behaviour matrix which we were not intending to affect. Hence self-organizing systems, although they are Markovian and highly predictable over certain periods of their history, at

Behaviour matrix of dog trained to show behaviour A in response to the light being on (Matrix V, 3)

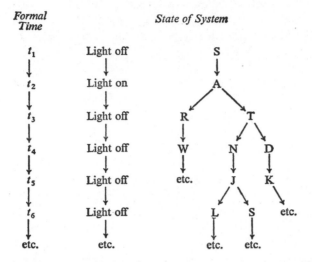

Since the animal has been trained only to do A in response to the light, neither B nor C, nor therefore any other behaviours which used to follow them are now available to it. Behaviour L can only be reached by a very much less direct route than before. Certain behaviour has vanished completely—for example behaviours F, X, and Z.

other times suddenly change in ways which, because we cannot look inside them to see how they are organized, are quite unpredictable.

An analogy which may clarify the point is the distribution of traffic flowing through a city. If we suddenly open a new by-pass, or close a road which usually carries a considerable amount of traffic, quite unforeseen effects may arise. We do not merely, say, prevent traffic going along one street. The cars which must now go round through the side streets increase the traffic density there. This may cause traffic jams in places where there have never been traffic jams before. To avoid these, people, who used to drive along those streets, in their turn start using yet other alternative routes, and the pattern of traffic flow throughout the city alters, until it reaches a new equilibrium situation where conditions are the most bearable for all drivers involved.

The brain is in some respects similar to this city. The nerve cells of which it is composed convey messages from sense organs, to muscles, from motivation centres, to arousal centres, and so on. The pathways along which these messages travel (the nerve fibres), are many more than the number of nerve cells, and possibly of the order of 10,000,000,000,000,000,000 in number. Each may make a junction with many other cells. And the resulting network is incredibly complex. Consequently, when we change the properties of one part of it, the effects may be rather unforeseen; while at the same time, paradoxically, but in line with other more complicated cybernetic ideas with which we have not dealt, such a system can sustain a remarkable amount of damage and still not show many signs of being effected. After all, even though many streets in a big city are closed by damage or snow, it is still usually possible for through traffic to get from one end of it to the other. (Psychologists and physiologists will here think of the Principle of Mass Action.)

Moreover, we know that the "wiring diagram" of the brain, the order and pattern in which the nerve cells are connected is not complete at birth, and indeed is not entirely determined by heredity, but at least in part by the use which the organism makes of its brain as it grows up. So in so far as each brain organizes itself as it develops, even a detailed knowledge of neuroanatomy will not give us a complete account of the organism's nature. For every time it alters its behaviour, learns, or forgets something, not merely the cells directly involved, but the whole equilibrium, the organization of the entire brain, is in some tiny degree, changed.

It is for this reason that self-organizing machines are both very difficult to analyse, but also very interesting and possess great potentialities. For although we start them off with certain properties, they may in time come to show properties which we did not realize were within their capabilities, and which can be put to use. (Think of the difference in a human being before and after being educated: and yet no new brain cells have been added, and indeed after the first few years of life they are being lost and not replaced, at a rate of some 100,000 or more per day!)

We are familiar with this in day-to-day life in many ways. For what we think of as getting to know people, or adopting the norms of society, and so on, may be described in terms of working out the behaviour matrices of those around us, and so altering our own as to make those of others go from one state which is desirable to another similar state and eliminating, or reducing at least, the probability of the occurrence of un-desirable states. The task of the science of psychology is to determine the general laws which best describe the structure of the behaviour maps of human behaviour. The job of the physiologist is to examine the wiring of the system.

Now this unpredictability in most living organisms, owing to their capacity to learn, is rather familiar in our everyday life, although the reason why it is so important, and the extent to which it guarantees unpredictability to most living organisms, the way of talking about it, is new since the coming of cyber-netics. But as yet the idea of machines showing this kind of behaviour is relatively unfamiliar. Generally in the past, throughout the birth of the machine age in the industrial revolution, the aim of designers has been to make the machines determinate as far as possible. Human performance was analysed, and the machine was designed to duplicate exactly what the human did. On the whole this is a fairly good strategy, and its only fault is that it does not make full use of the machine, for the latter is limited by the *detailed* knowledge and insight of the designer, even though in principle we can make components which are better at their job than humans. There are just beginning to be a few machines which are not determinate, and which learn for themselves how to perform a task, having merely been told what is wanted.

A very simple device of this kind is easy to imagine. Consider our old friend the thermostat again. The job of this device is to maintain temperature constant between certain agreed limits. We do not usually mind if the temperature goes up or down one degree, but we object to it going up or down five degrees if we have gone to the trouble of installing central heating. So generally what we do is to install a thermostat. If the temperature falls more than two degrees below the temperature for which it is set, it turns the heat up; if it rises more than two degrees, it turns it down. But such a device is not really very efficient. There is bound to be a time-lag between turning up the heat and its having its effect, so the temperature in fact fluctuates more than the thermostat is meant to allow. We could, of course, buy a more sensitive thermostat, and control it even more closely. But with a self-organizing system there is the possibility of even doing away with the lag, so that the temperature is more closely controlled than we could expect from a machine which did not learn.

Consider a thermostat which as well as controlling the temperature also kept a record of how it varied. Such a record would show several features. For example, shortly after the heating was turned up there would be a relatively quick rise in the temperature, which would overshoot the desired temperature, and then, when the heat was turned down, the temperature would slowly fall again. Now we can well imagine that there might be other very important regularities. Perhaps we might observe that only if the temperature fell rather slowly did it ever go all the way down: short quick drops always went up again. (These might for example be due to someone momentarily opening a door.) While if a drop of as little as half a degree had occurred over several minutes, this meant that the temperature would, in another twenty minutes, be so low that the heating would have to be turned on. In fact, it is quite likely that, for a given house, there would be features about the temperature fluctuations which allowed us to predict what was going to happen. Now we have already seen that it is possible to build artefacts to recognize patterns. So we could build one which could detect regularities in the record of the temperature. And if the regularities were of the form "a slow fall of $\frac{1}{2}°$ always means the temperature becomes too low 20 minutes later", then we could in principle make the machine learn how to prevent the temperature ever falling so low. We arrange it so that whenever a slow fall comes, it alters the switch which controls the heat. At first it does this randomly, so that the temperature is just as likely to fall as to rise. But we also arrange that it then stores a record of what it has done (perhaps on magnetic tape), and whenever the time after which the heater has to be turned up is shorter than the average, then it records this and throws a switch so that that particular setting is never used again. It will be clear that large falls of temperature will gradually be eliminated, for essentially the system predicts what is going to happen and only keeps those responses which lead to more successful predictions. A similar system would deal with too great a rise.

Now of course this is a case of "feedback" once again. The system predicts what the temperature is going to do, just as the radar-controlled gun predicted where the aircraft was going to be. And using feedback, to check its success as a predictor (in this case the subsequent change of temperature as registered by the thermometer), the system can get better and better, so that its errors become fewer. The time lag can be done away with by predicting in advance what is going to happen, and taking action before it occurs.

It is true that we should not think this a very "intelligent" way of solving the problem, this use of random responses as a basis for adaptation. But there is nothing but "trial and error", which is available even for a human being when problem solving, if the solver does not know anything about the problem in the first place. And the point at issue was not that the machine was particularly clever, but that it learnt. Such a system as the one we have been discussing has a fair title to being described as a machine which learns. Initially it has a wide repertoire of responses, and this repertoire is gradually narrowed down by trial and error until only the optimal responses are left. Either it learns, or (again for the benefit of the tough-minded purist), it "behaves as if it were learning". (Note that the only way we can find out if a human has learnt is to see whether, either verbally or non-verbally, he behaves as if he were learning. And if, on the basis of what he does, we decide that such a human has learnt, it seems hard to refuse the same label to the performance of the machine. No metaphysical questions arise at this point.)

It is clear that it would be grossly uneconomical to build a self-organizing system of any degree of complexity merely in order to control the temperature of a dwelling house, but such machines are today being designed for industrial purposes. For example, in the control of chemical distillation plants it is often the case that to change the temperature of one part of the distillation column has far-reaching effects which are not confined to the part of the system which we actually want to adjust. (Here the analogy of the changes in traffic flow following the blocking of one street comes to mind again.) Very often the system is so complex that the outcome of making an adjustment to one part of the system is impossible in detail to predict. Where the situation is sufficiently complex, a machine which learns by trial and error, with none of the fallibility of human memory, may well be the most economical form of control mechanism. It could begin (as in the example which we gave in an earlier chapter) by learning from a human who had been looking after the control process for some time and was skilled, and then go on from that point to improve its performance. It is likely that such machines will become common over the next fifty years.

We may similarly show that it is possible to construct a machine which shows "goal-seeking" behaviour. An artefact of this type would appear to an observer to be purposeful, in the way which an animal showing instinctive behaviour appears to be purposeful. We generally think of such behaviour as being that in which there is some quite well defined act to which the behaviour of the animal appears to be driving it, and where, once this act has been performed the activity ceases. For example, a hungry animal moves about until it has eaten, a thirsty one until it has drunk, and in the mating season the male moves about in search of the female until mating has been completed by copulation. We recognize behaviour of this type in the animal world as being purposive. In the comparative psychology laboratory we can make various other behaviours become purposive. An animal will learn to run through a maze without making any errors if it is always fed when it gets to the end of the maze. In the wild the flight of a bat is purposive, in that it is hunting for its food, insects, on the wing. And on the complicated flickering flight path along which it travels it is guided by the echoes of its squeaks from the bodies of the insects which form its prey, and it uses this feedback to control the direction of its flight so that it closes in on the insect.

Now we have seen an artefact which shows this last kind of purposive behaviour already in the self-guided missile, which acts exactly in the same way. The missile does not know that it is hunting down an aircraft, but nor does the bat, in the sense that it does not say to itself, "Ah! An insect!" but simply responds blindly with its reflex responses to the signals it receives through its ears. A mechanistic account is entirely adequate for biology, providing it is realized that the scope of mechanism is not limited to the kick-it-and-it-will-move kind of causal model, but embraces the possibility of Markovian and self-organizing mechanisms. A mechanism of the maze-learning variety has been designed and built by Deutsch, to demonstrate his theory of animal learning. His "mechanical rat" can

learn a T-shaped maze of some complexity, in that it begins
by entering blind alleys just as often as correct ones, but comes
to enter only the correct ones after a few runs through the
maze. If the maze is a double-T in succession, the "rat" can
learn each half separately, and then, when the two parts are
joined, it will go correctly through the whole maze on the first
occasion it is put in providing only that the two have some one
point on the correct route in common. Furthermore, if a short-
cut which by-passes parts of the maze is introduced, providing
that it is possible to see the other end of the short-cut from the
beginning of it, the "rat" will take the short-cut in preference
to the usual route on the first occasion it comes across it: it
shows "insight" in just the way that the real animals do in such
a situation.

Having used this word "insight" to describe the behaviour
of animals and artefacts which are capable of making use of
material which is suddenly provided without the necessity of
further learning, it might be as well to pause for a moment to
consider certain questions which arise about the use of language. There are many words, such as "intellect", "intelligence", even "soul" which were used by the scholastic
philosophers in a special sense, a sense which amounted to
these words being carefully defined technical terms—terms as
technical as "atom", "neutron" and "electron" are to the
atomic physicist. Originally, the technical terms were in Latin;
but they have been translated by modern equivalents which
already have a use in our language. It is abundantly clear that
words such as *intelligence* cannot be correctly translated by
just using the transliteration into English. "Intelligent" nowadays very often simply means "scoring highly on I.Q. tests",
a meaning which has no contact with the scholastic technical
use of the term. As a friend once jokingly remarked, the I.Q.
of God could only be 100, or average; for the I.Q. is the ratio
of mental age to chronological age, and although God is
infinitely wise he is also infinitely old! It is absolutely essential

not to reject the idea of machines showing "intelligent behaviour", "insight", and so on, simply because these words
have been used to translate technical terms of medieval
philosophy. The use of "insight", "intelligence", "concept",
and so on, which we are discussing, is the use of language *in
our own time* regardless of what these words may have meant
in the past. When I claim that a machine can show insight, I
am not referring to the kind of thing of which Fr Lonnergan
wrote in his book of that title, but to what people nowadays
mean when they say that a person or animal "suddenly saw
the answer in a flash", rather than finding the solution tediously
by trial-and-error methods. The root of much of the fruitless
philosophical controversy between neo-scholastics, and in
particular educated Catholics who are not professional philosophers, and their secular opponents is that all too often the
Catholics appear to think that the English transliteration of
a scholastic Latin term is the only meaning which the English
version has, rather than realizing that such a use is in fact highly
eccentric in the middle of the twentieth century, and has to be
carefully defined if people are not to understand it in its more
usual, everyday, sense.

Trial-and-error is not, however, to be despised, for it is
essentially the best method which is open to a self-organizing
system to acquire its organization. We give the machine the
criterion for success (the temperature must not fluctuate more
than $\frac{1}{2}°$; traffic must leave the city at a rate of 5,000 cars per
hour) and then let it try all the possible behaviours (strategies)
that are open to it, and by using feedback find which lead most
quickly or most nearly to the desired criterion. Furthermore,
since it has feedback, and the possibility of continuing to try
new strategies, a self-organizing system will not usually get
into a fixed habit (although certain cases do arise when this can
happen). Such machines will show "purposive behaviour", for
their behaviour will, as it were, "close in on" the region of
action in which the criterion lies, and viewed from outside we

shall see a constantly changing pattern of behaviour which gradually becomes more and more stable as the criterion is approached, occasionally shows sudden insightful jumps, and, once the criterion has been reached, settles down to a repetition of the optimal behaviour.

Such machines are sometimes called "hill-climbing systems". This is because a useful model for them is that of a region in which there is a hill, whose summit it is desired to reach. A blind man who could not see the shape of the land could get to the top by walking randomly, providing that he obeyed one rule only: "whenever you do not feel yourself walking uphill, walk in some other direction". It is clear that he can choose his direction to walk in at random; but providing this instruction is obeyed he will inevitably make his way to higher and higher ground, until at last he stands on the topmost peak. And there he will stay, for in every direction in which he walks he will feel himself going downhill and so will turn and try another. This is essentially what our problem-solving artefact does when it tries one course of action after another at random, keeping only those which bring it nearer than it was before to the criterion of success. The only kind of terrain on which the blind man could fail would be one in which there was a secondary, lower peak. For once he got on to the slopes of that one, rather than the slopes of the main peak, he would inevitably reach the summit of the lower peak, and there, as shown above, he would stay and never find the bigger. In the same way, if there is a type of behaviour which is fairly good as a solution to some problem, and one from which any departure is worse than to stay there, it would be impossible for a machine to stop doing this once it had got that far, even though there might be a much better solution some distance away on its behavioural map. This is the case which was mentioned above of a possible failure of trial-and-error to solve a problem completely. A possible, though drastic way out would be to force the artefact to make occasional very big random variations in its behaviour, which would transport it bodily to some new kind of behaviour, from which point it would start its solution-seeking all over again, and might on occasion find a better way.

When we have been talking of animals which learn, show insightful behaviour, purposive behaviour, and so on, we have been talking, of course, of animals which show *adaptive* behaviour. Such behaviour is the basis of self-preservation. And to this extent we can also describe our artefacts as being adaptive. And also, therefore, it becomes possible to envisage ones which are self-preserving, or self-maintaining. There is first of all the rather trivial sense in which we can imagine an artefact which, if a valve or a transistor burnt out, would replace it with another from a stock with which it was supplied. But there is a much more interesting sense in which it is possible to design self-preserving machines. Consider again the *Machina Speculatrix* which Grey Walter built. This was, it will be re-called, an artefact looking like a tortoise which was sensitive to light, and tended to approach light. Such a system could be made to show self-preserving properties in this way. Let its outer surface be covered by photo-electric cells, which generate electricity whenever light falls on them. If we connected them to the batteries which drive the "tortoise", then it would keep its own batteries charged, for it would always tend to go towards light, and so when it reached it the energy it had used to get there would be replenished by the electricity generated by its photocells. The other thing it would need would be fresh water to "top up" its battery from time to time, and as Grey Walter has pointed out, it could get this from dew at night. Probably it would have to go somewhere different from where the light is brightest in the daytime in order to collect a heavy dew, but this could be done by using the electricity stored during the day and giving it a device which was sensitive to the degree of dampness in the air. The modified *Machina Speculatrix* would then shuttle back and forth between bright sunny spots (not always the same one) in the daytime, and cool, dewy regions (not always the same one) at night. Such behaviour would be self-preserving in a very real sense, since the acquisition of energy and the maintenance of the fluids in the system are *exactly* what animals do in feeding and drinking. We do not want to say that such a system is alive, but we certainly have here in a very real sense a self-preserving system which is an artefact, and an account of the logic of self-preservation which does not necessitate any supposed extra properties which living matter has over non-living matter. I shall shortly argue that living systems anyway have no properties which prevent their synthesis from non-living matter.

We see then, that self-preservation, or "homeostasis" as it is often called, is within the province of an artefact. But this is self-preservation of an *individual*, both in the case of the animal and of the artefact. We may also talk of the homeostasis of a species as such. This is what we see in the world around us. When a species is threatened with extinction, it is because the homeostatic control of the species is failing.

Essentially the problem of self-preservation is one of maintaining a state of equilibrium. The metabolic activities of an organism, or the mechanical and electrical functions of an artefact, are constantly using up energy, and in order for the system to survive, this must be replaced from the environment. The energy requirements of the system must be kept in balance. When this fails the animal eventually dies and the artefact runs down, and stops. In the same way, in order for a species to maintain itself in existence, the members must be replaced, for the whole time some are dying, others being killed, or failing to find mates, and some are born sterile; so that over all there is a constant drain on the membership of the species. This is usually made good by the birth-rate, and the balance between births and deaths results in homeostasis of the species and the maintenance of equilibrium. Where the death-rate rises without the birth-rate rising, from whatever the cause, then homeostasis fails and unless the species modifies either its breeding habits (so that it breeds faster), or its behavioural habits (so that its predators are no longer so effective), or its habitat (so that the cause of death is left behind), then it will become extinct. The self-preservation of that system which is the species as a whole consists in the adaptation of the system, its changing its properties, so that the problem of equating the birth-rate with the death-rate is solved.

We can argue along the lines we suggested before for the solution of problems by any adaptive system. What the species should do (what the system should do) is to make random variations in its behaviour, and keep those which tend toward the desirable goal. And in fact this is what happens. Mutations, and the mixing of genetic hereditary material by random mating, plus the accidents of different amounts of food, and so on, result in every member of a species being slightly different from every other. Some will be slightly faster than average, some quicker learners, some inflexible in their habits, some less ready to mate than most. And the environment will take its toll accordingly. The slightly faster ones will tend to escape more frequently from predators, and if they happen to be more fertile than most, the species as a whole will slowly become better at escaping from their predators, and will be more adaptive to the environment. On the other hand, homeostasis of the species could equally well be maintained by slower animals which bred very much faster and had larger families, so that even though large numbers were killed by predators, there would still be enough to survive.

In short, the random genetic mutations, intermingling of hereditary material by interbreeding, and chance factors such as diet, produce just the series of random changes in the properties of the system (species) *taken as a whole*, which we have seen is the way to construct an adaptive machine which will solve the problem of homeostasis. And the action of the environment, malnutrition, predators, etc., provides the way

construct a copy of itself if the instructions are correct. Right at the end of the process the programme reads as follows. "Copy these instructions and feed the copy into the new computer. Now switch it on. Now cut it loose from yourself." When these instructions have all been carried out the new computer will in its turn reproduce, for it is now in operation with the same programme (set of instructions) as the previous one. Self-reproduction by artefacts is therefore in principle possible. In fact a small system with these properties has been produced by Penfield, although it is not a giant computer, but a small toy made of wood and metal. In this device the shape of the levers and the pieces of wood of which it is made is the way in which the programming is carried out. Put into an environment where there are many of its parts, such a system will make more and more of itself at the expense of the materials available in the environment.

It may be objected that this account is misleading in that the component parts have to be available, whereas living systems which reproduce themselves do not need such parts. This objection is mistaken. Whenever an organism eats and drinks it is taking its component parts into itself (protein, fat, carbohydrate molecules of various kinds) just as surely as the artefact. There are even some substances, such as the vitamins and the so-called "essential amino-acids" which certain species cannot manufacture from their food, but *must* find ready-made in that food if they are to survive. The process is exactly comparable. Moreover, in the reproduction of one organism from another an exactly similar process takes place. The materials are assembled during sexual intercourse (in bisexual species), and by the passage of nutritive materials from the mother to the embryo during the foetal life in the uterus.

We see, then, that reproduction by artefacts is possible. Hence it is possible that they may evolve. (It must be remembered throughout that these are logical, not practical possibilities. Particularly in the case of the topics about to be discussed, the expense would be so enormous that such a thing would never be attempted. We are not, however, interested in practical limitations but in the logical limitations and their meaning. And what follows is logically possible.)

To achieve evolution in an artefact, we must first decide on the criterion for fitness. Let us suppose that we want a system that will compute mathematical calculations faster than existing systems. We design a computer which is both a calculating machine and also self-reproductive. We then include in its programme two new stages. Firstly, we require it to measure how long certain calculations take and to pass this information on to its descendants. Next, in the instructions for assembling its descendants we include the step, "Allow 1 per cent random variation in the wiring diagram". This means that its descendants will not be exactly like itself, but that in each generation, indeed in each offspring, there will be slight changes. Finally, we arrange that one of the instructions is, "If the time taken to perform the test calculations is less than that which was passed on from the previous generation, retain the last change which has been made in the wiring diagram".

Most of the descendants of the parent computer will not work, for even 1 per cent random variation will cause the wiring to short circuit, or at least not calculate properly. (This is analogous to the usually deleterious effect of mutations in organisms.) But here and there there will be one which does work, although different from its predecessors. And by chance the connections which arise in its wiring may make new kinds of mathematical operations possible which were not available to the older machines. Hence new ways of performing calculations will arise, and it is possible that ways which not even the designer of the parent machine knew will appear by chance. And it may be that these will enable the calculations to be done faster. This would be a machine which evolved. Indeed, in the long run, except for the problems which are very simple, and which there were only one or two ways of solving, an evolving system would be bound to do better than its designers. But it would take many generations, and, as was mentioned, it is not a practical possibility because of the enormous number of "lethal" mutations which would appear, making the machines containing them worthless except to be broken up and used again for raw materials. It would, however, be possible for a machine to emerge which was substantially cleverer than its designer. In principle it is possible to get out of such a system behaviour of a more complex order than its designer, even if human, could show.

Two more problems remain to be discussed in this chapter. The first follows directly from the last section, the other, concerning the cybernetic analysis of social reform, is entirely different, and serves, as well as a warning to utopians, to illustrate the scope of the conceptual methods.

Firstly however, let us look at the question of the possibility of the artificial synthesis of life, for clearly it is related rather closely to the question of self-replication by artefacts, which is the least we should expect from any system to which the name "living" might be applied, although it had been synthesized.

It is a matter of some historical curiosity, as was pointed out to the writer by Fr Anthony Kenny, that we find it so difficult today to accept the idea that life can be synthesized. If we turn to the medieval scholastics, such as Aquinas, we find that they firmly believed that such an event was not merely possible, but frequent. Their empirical evidence was completely wrong—they adduced such facts as the emergence of maggots from dead meat—but they saw no logical objection to the idea. This alone should do much to make us wary of the extraordinary resistance to the idea which is prevalent among Christians today. It appears that the experiments of Pasteur in the nineteenth century, in which he showed that micro-organisms did not arise in solutions unless other micro-organisms were already present, mark the moment after which the idea of the synthesis of life or its spontaneous appearance suddenly became completely unacceptable. Unfortunately Pasteur's work was in the context of an argument with a rationalist scientist, and the issue of whether life could arise spontaneously became confused with the religious argument. The argument really had no relevance to whether the spontaneous appearance of life was a possibility or not in *principle*: it merely showed that what had been thought to be an example was, like the maggots in the meat, not one after all.

Bearing in mind then that there has never in the tradition of Christian philosophy been any surprise at or doubt of the possibility (merely as a way of reducing our prejudices against the idea) let us consider how such a task as the synthesis of a living system could be achieved in principle.

The marks which are the characteristic of living systems are usually given as self-reproduction, the power of locomotion, the taking in of energy and the building up of organization (anabolism), sensitivity, and "immanent activity" (which seems to mean that activity arises from the organism itself and not in response to an external stimulus: the phrase is generally used to contrast with reflex action, or in contrast to the kind of "push-pull" response of a billiard ball hit by a cue).

Of these we have seen that it is possible to make devices which are sensitive (even a thermostat is sensitive, to heat); show immanent activity and locomotion (the *Machina Speculatrix* which begins to search for light and water to offset its energy deficits); and even anabolism and self-reproduction (*Machina Speculatrix* and the account of self-reproducing computers). The implication is clear that it is theoretically possible to produce an artefact which has each of the characteristics which we associate with living systems. And hence that there is no reason in principle to stop us producing one which has them all. Such an artefact would be one which we would find it hard to accept as alive mainly because we have so far talked as if we would always build in metals, glass and plastics. But there is of course nothing to stop us building "chemical computers" (in which, for example, we would perform addition by adding quantities of chemicals and weighing the precipitate formed to get the answer). And there is nothing to stop us in principle using "organic" components. Certain amino-acids (the constituents of protein molecules) have already been synthesized in the laboratory, and it is only a question of time and money before it becomes possible to synthesize any protein we like. We then could use proteins as the components out of which we could make our artefact which was to be "living". And now the last objection would be removed, for it would even be built out of artificial biological materials. (This is, of course, what usually happens in reproduction. When we synthesize a living system, we bring the chemical components together in one way, in test-tubes. Normally the components are assembled by eating, drinking, and then mating behaviour.)

We may conclude that, logically at least, the design of a synthetic living system is comparatively simple. We may also look at the question another way. We have seen that one of the characteristics of living systems is that they are "self-organizing systems". We have seen that it is quite easy to design simple self-organizing systems (for example the learning machines which we discussed earlier). Now the self-organizing machines which we build are built of inert bits and pieces: it is only the combination of these bits and pieces which has the properties of the system. Normally we build the system by designing with great care, and building with a high degree of accuracy. But it is imaginable, though extremely unlikely, that if we put all the components in a box and just shook them up together, they might, if we tried again and again, happen to fall into the pattern of organization which showed self-organizing properties. This would also hold for that particular class of self-organizing system which was self-reproducing, and indeed, alive. This is a possible account of the emergence, in the earlier years of the earth's history, of living from non-living material. It may not have happened that way, but it clearly could have. At this distance of time we cannot decide for certain on scientific evidence. But there is no need to postulate any supernatural happening to account for systems with the properties which we observe in living systems arising from non-living systems. The problem in philosophical theology is not to account for the sudden appearance of systems with souls, that is, living systems (for that is what having a soul means—see *Summa Theologica*, Ia, qu. 75); but to account for the appearance of the properties which we see in the human soul, that is, for the appearance of a particular class of living system, that which we usually call "human".

Finally, we turn our attention to the system which we generally call "society", and which in some ways is rather like a "species", which, as we saw earlier, can be treated as a self-preserving, self-organizing, system, whose parts are rather loosely connected to one another. It is true that in a society, the components (the people) are joined to one another by rather unusual connections. These connections are the mutually interdependent needs of the members, the rules and conventions of the society, and the design of living conditions (a green belt around a city prevents certain kinds of relations between country dwellers and city dwellers arising), and so on. But we can, nonetheless, make a behaviour map, or matrix, of the states of a society from one moment in history to the next (remember how in Chapter I we saw that a list of the rulers of a country and their dates is one such matrix), although it is probably in practice impossible to give a complete analysis, unless the states which we use in the analysis are very inclusive and not very detailed. Now it might be thought that by analysing this matrix we could find certain areas in it which are undesirable, and that this analysis could be the basis for social reform. But this is a mistake, and moreover is the mistake made by every reformer who envisages a utopian society. The data of sociological surveys do in fact amount to a behaviour matrix. When we discover that, perhaps, delinquency is high in people from slum housing areas, we have as it were drawn in one transition in the matrix, which goes

"... (t_1) living in slums (t_2) delinquent behaviour p_1
(t_2) no   „   „ p_2"

where p_1 and p_2 are the probabilities of the two classes of behaviour and in this case p_1 is much greater than p_2.

Now if the system we call society were state-determined, or even a stable Markovian system, the answer for the social reformer would be obvious—remove slums and all will be well. For then that path through the behaviour matrix would be closed, so that the later states could not be reached. In practice, of course, there are many behaviour paths through the matrix of the history of a society which lead to the same point. But in principle it might be possible to map out the matrix and close all these paths one by one. We would then hope that all would be well—the particular undesirable behaviour would have been removed from the society. But, unfortunately, this can never be the case. In the early parts of this chapter we saw that when you change one part of a self-organizing system which has a very richly connected organization, then you cannot be sure what the result will be, for the whole of the organization of the system will change to a greater or lesser degree until a new equilibrium is reached. Such a system is Society. When we reform it, when we carry out *all* the desirable reforms, we shall not end up with a utopia. For the properties of our new society will be so different that we shall be unable to foresee them, and while we shall have removed certain areas of disequilibrium in the system, new ones which are in principle unforeseeable will arise, and have in their turn to be dealt with. The search for utopia is doomed to failure, not because of some inherent nastiness in human nature, not because of our lack of wisdom and foresight but because the system we are members of, and which we call "Society", is a complex, richly interconnected, self-organizing system, and is bound to produce unpredictable behaviour in response to changes made in its states and attributes.

CHAPTER VI

MAN AND MACHINES: THE IMPLICATIONS OF CYBERNETICS

Pattern recognizers have been made. Purposive artefacts are now commonplace in weapons systems. Machine translation is approaching a solution, adaptive artefacts are on the drawing boards, and in biochemical laboratories the synthesis of a living system will almost certainly be achieved within the next five or ten years at the latest. We have seen that our analysis of the world in cybernetic language leads to some unusual and extremely striking conclusions. Throughout the discussion we have emphasized that the difficulties in making artefacts perform specified behaviours is one of technology, and therefore uninteresting to us, and not a logical difficulty. We do not have to wait for better transistors, valves, and electronic materials to discuss what artefacts can do: we can design them on paper, and that is sufficient to follow out the implications of the theory of artefacts for the understanding of the world and for modelling it. We can, in short, discuss the ultimate limits of the science of cybernetics without waiting for the construction of actual machines. Where do these limits lie?

Two theories in cybernetic logic are outstandingly important in examining this question, and it is on these theorems that we shall centre our attention. Some years ago, an English logician called Turing tried to obtain a formal definition of any conceivable machine. The description[1] which he gave ran as follows: "*If we have a system which can be in one of several states, together with a list of those states, and the rules for getting from one state to another, then we have a machine.*" Those who are familiar with the philosophy of science will notice that this has a marked resemblance to the structure of a scientific theory, where we usually have a list of postulates about the hypothetical constructs involved in the theory, together with a set of rules for how the constructs interact. We shall see later that this similarity has important consequences for the nature of social science. The description given by Turing covers all those systems in the world to which we usually give the name of machine.

The second important theorem was developed some time later by two men, W. S. McCulloch and W. Pitts, who have worked for a long time on the analysis and simulation of nerve networks. They set out to invent a model nervous system. They described units that were certainly much simpler than real nerve cells are, and asked the question, "Given as many of these 'model neurones' as we want, what can we make a network of them do?" Since the units they were working with are simpler than real neurones, we may conclude that if they had found that there were severe limits on the abilities of their "model nervous systems", they might have been able to get over these difficulties by making their neurones more complicated. But in fact that proved to be unnecessary. For the analysis they were able to produce of their *model networks* showed that they *can perform ANY behaviour which can be described in a finite number of words.*

It appears that this, and this alone, defines the boundary of possibilities of any artefact which we can make: this is the limit of the synthetic Turing machine.

[1] The given description is a "popular" account of the implications of Turing's original analysis.   The formal logical derivation can be found in the references given at the back of this book.

The importance of the two theorems will at once be clear. It is because of Turing's theorem that we do not need to wait for the advance of technology to provide us with better machines to see what the limits of machines will be. For Turing has described all conceivable machines, and hence we can examine the implications of any conceivable machine, even though such a one cannot as yet be built. If we can determine the properties of all Turing machines, we shall know the limits of which any machine will be capable in the future. Furthermore, the results of McCulloch and Pitts provide us with the method. For their model nervous networks are certainly Turing machines. And Turing was able to provide one rather remarkable and extremely important property of such machines. *It is possible to describe an artefact which can do anything an even more complex artefact can do.* It therefore becomes impossible to argue that simply because a brain, say, is larger and more complex than any system of which we have experience, that therefore it will turn out to have special unknown and irreproducible properties. Instead, we must concentrate our attention on what a "universal" artefact can do. A "universal" artefact is one which can do anything even a more complex and bigger one can do.

We have seen that McCulloch and Pitts were able to show that the limit on such systems was that they could show any behaviour which can be described in a finite number of words. And this is the key to the problem. There are, in a sense, two keys, for it will be noticed upon inspection that there are two sections into which the statement falls. In the first place, it is concerned with *behaviour*. The universal artefact will be able to show "any *behaviour* which can be described in a finite number of words". And secondly, there is the qualification about the description of that behaviour; the artefact will show any behaviour "which can be described *in a finite number of words*". Both of these impose quite stringent limits on our deliberate attempts to construct what have been called "humanoid" artefacts, for while we have already come across the first, even the second is widespread in its implications. There are many aspects of human behaviour which appear not to be describable in "a finite number of words".

As far as anyone has analysed the problem, this theorem of McCulloch and Pitts seems to be the boundary. If there are no events in the natural history of humans which are beyond it, then it is in principle possible to construct a human being. If such events do exist, then it is in principle impossible. Little work has been done on the logical analysis of this field, even in the last few years. But at present that seems to be the situation. It is impossible to appeal to the "spirituality" of human nature as an argument against the possibility of constructing "human" artefacts, for the following reason. We have no direct knowledge or evidence for such spirituality. We can only conclude that other people seem to have the same nature as we have from what they do and say. And with regard to our own life and nature, all we can do is to be aware of our experiences and to be aware of doing things. But self-awareness, and introspection about it, do not lead to any evidence for there being a part of man which is "non-material", "survives after death", and so on. The claim for some supernatural part of human nature never was, when defended most skilfully, founded on direct experience of this part of his nature. It is true that this is what is currently done in most arguments between materialists and their opponents, and that telepathy, ghosts, and all sorts of data clutter up such disputes. But this is due to the malign influence of Descartes upon the development of Western Christian thought in the last few centuries. Previously the arguments had, at their best, been based on deductions about behaviour and experience. Their form was, "If there is an organism which behaves in such and such a way, and can make certain uses of its experiences in such and such a way, it must have properties which cannot be described exhaustively in spatio-temporal terms". That is all the claim to supernatural qualities in man can amount to in natural philosophy. Now it is not immediately obvious that such events are not within the framework of the McCulloch-Pitts theorem, nor that it is impossible to design an artefact which would show the same sorts of behaviour. We shall therefore leave aside any such considerations, and simply turn to the implications of the McCulloch-Pitts theorem.

Let us first consider the word "behaviour". We can design an artefact to show any *behaviour*. . . .

We have met this limitation before. It will be recalled that we have had, when talking both of the performances of animals and of possible artefacts, to bring in the qualification that they behaved "as if" they were having certain experiences. The pattern recognizer behaved "as if" it were perceiving the shape as we do; the dog moved "as if" it were dreaming. And although by convention we drop this phrase out of conversation when we speak of the performance of animals in everyday life, it is always there as a tacit assumption. For we can never share the experience of either another animal or even another human being. In fact, as we have said, we cannot tell, except by their overt behaviour (either verbal or non-verbal) that another person has had an experience. If, for example, we record the electrical brain rhythms of a human, and discover that whenever a certain pattern occurs he says he has seen a light, we have not thereby recorded his experience; merely another kind of event, the behaviour of his brain cells. The only way we can be sure that he has had the experience of seeing a light is by asking him to report somehow on his experience (although in practice people almost always do report their experiences when their behaviour leads us to expect it). Perceptions, other than our own, are logically private. I know that other animals and other men have perceived a light, or heard a sound, or seen a triangle, by their behaviour, but I know that I have perceived a light, or heard a sound, or seen a triangle simply by having the experience.

This "having an experience" is one of the things which we cannot deliberately design a machine to do. For to have an experience is not to do anything, not to show any sort of behaviour. It is true that we could build a machine that could tell us that it had seen a light. We could arrange that when its photoreceptors sent an impulse of more than a certain value into the artefact, then a record would be activated, and the machine would tell us that it had seen a light. But this would have to be done by measuring the amount of activity in the photoreceptors. This would correspond to our deciding that we had seen a light by knowing that the nerves between our eyes and our brain were unusually highly activated. But this is precisely what we do not do; rather, we know that our nerves have been activated because we have seen a light, otherwise, it would mean that no one would be able to know that they had seen a light who did not know about neurology, a situation which is patently false. No, we can design artefacts which *behave as if* they were having experiences, but that is in principle as far as we can go. Experience is not the same as behaving, and when we try to give an account of what sequence of states the parts of the artefact must go through to have an experience, we find the problem insoluble, for the ultimate criterion for the occurrence of a system having an experience is simply its having one, not any particular part of its behaviour or electrical activity which would lead us to conclude that it had had one. Note, though, that it is true that what causes us in some way to have any experience is electrical activity in our nerve cells.

It is this discrepancy between experience and behaviour which makes us to say that man has a mind, has mental experiences, performs mental acts. To have a mind does not mean that there is any intangible body (the "self" or "ego") which is stuck just inside the skin of the tangible body. It means that it is possible to imagine a situation in which the overt behaviour pointed to one sort of occurrence, but where we could find that something else was the case, by asking the person about what had occurred. And it is because having an experience is not the same as behaving that it is impossible to make an artefact which has a mind.

It is worth pausing to note that while it is impossible to make an artefact which has experiences by deliberately designing it, because the behaviour matrix for having experiences is not a thing which can be drawn up, an artefact of this type might appear by accident. We do not know what it is about the construction of the human nervous system, about the design of a human being, which conveys upon it the property of not merely behaving but also having experiences. But it is quite conceivable that one day when an artefact was being constructed for another purpose, we might discover that it was showing verbal and non-verbal behaviour of the kind that in humans makes us say that they are having experiences. Whether such a thing could happen is not within the province of science, whether cybernetics or other sciences, to say. But it does not seem excluded by the present analysis. Indeed, one must assume that this is what has happened during the evolution of the human body. The Christian will want to say that the particular principle of organization which carries with it the peculiar properties of man arose through the intervention of God to ensure that the correct kind of nervous system was selected in the course of evolution, and will also say that there is some kind of qualitative discontinuity in the process. It is not clear from Christian philosophy as yet exactly what sort of account can be given of this discontinuity, which is covered by the usual remark that "each human soul is especially created".

It seems to the writer that it is an open question theologically whether an "experiencing artefact" could arise by chance. But it is quite clear that Revelation accords a unique status to man, in that it implies some radical difference between man and the other animals. It appears that theologically there is no particular objection to accepting that man has evolved from the other animals, in some sense. (As we saw, given the kind of reproductive behaviour and the kind of environment in which we live, evolution is not merely possible but inevitable.) But the meeting-ground of philosophy, theology, and science (in particular cybernetics) is over the question of the nature of the obvious discontinuity in the process which occurs when a system suddenly appears which has experiences as well as showing behaviour. We have used the word "behaviour" in this book to mean the states through which a system, any system (a boiling kettle, a running dog, a hunting man) moves in time. And behaviour, in this extended sense which cybernetics gives it, is the proper study of the various sciences. But "experience" is of a different logical class. It is possible to design a machine, an artefact, to behave as if it has experiences, but the most that we can do apart from this is to hope that one day one of them will suddenly report on itself in a way which corresponds to humans doing it. We cannot design for the latter, and it is impossible to say how it came about that the human system has this property.

If we now turn our attention to the second part of the McCulloch-Pitts theorem, we come to the phrase "any behaviour *which can be defined in a finite number of words*". It may seem strange that this is a limitation on the theory of any importance, for surely we know how to tell someone what to do? And if so, surely we can tell an artefact what to do?

Now there is one sense in which the theorem is true but trivial. It could be read to mean simply, "I can only make an artefact do something if I can tell it what to do." This is obviously true. Even random, "hill-climbing", trial-and-error behaviour by the machine will not achieve the desired result unless we tell it what the criterion of success is. But there is a much more important sense in which it must be accepted; and this imposes further limitations on what artefacts can be designed to do, and also has implications for the use of scientific method in examining certain problems.

Consider the word "belief". It is true that often, and indeed usually, we can tell what people believe by what they do, by their behaviour (either verbal or non-verbal). Hence it looks as if we should be able to make an artefact which "believes". But on closer inspection there is a curious evasiveness about the matrix of behaviour required for describing belief. For example, we may decide that a man believes that a building is on fire if he runs from it shouting "Fire!" But equally well we may decide that such is his belief if he runs *towards* it shouting "Fire!" if we know, for example, that he is a fireman. Indeed, if he is in between two buildings when he shouts and runs, *only* our background knowledge about the context in which the action is taking place (whether he is a fireman or not), will let us decide, from his behaviour, which building he thinks is on fire. To take a case that is familiar to social psychologists and sociologists, it is notoriously difficult to assess the extent of religious belief in a community. What behaviour do we use— the number of times people go to church?—but they may go because of social pressure. The number of nights on which they say prayers?—but they may do so to please their spouse, or may tell us a wrong number because they want to give "a respectable" answer. How intensely do they feel confident that they *do* believe?—but often people who say that they believe intensely do things in their everyday life which are blatantly incompatible with their stated beliefs. And so on. There is a curious elusiveness about the behavioural criteria for "belief", whether we are concerned with the verbal or the non-verbal, or both.

This elusiveness has been analysed by several modern philosophers, and had been remarked on many centuries ago by various authors. It is characteristic of those events in human natural history which Aquinas called *actus humani*, and has been raised by Peters under the heading of "those cases in which a person may be significantly said to do things" rather than just having things happen to him. Broadly speaking, the class of behaviour in question seems to cover all of that field of behaviour which we call "social", and both in Wittgenstein and in Winch (who follows him) we find the point that these behaviours need more than a straightforward description of the action in physical terms. For there are many different physical actions by which we may decide a man believes one thing. And some of these physical actions may be reasons for thinking that he is doing other things instead in other contexts. A man who is cutting down a tree may be making firewood, or clearing land to plough, or even building a boat. And without giving the context in which he is working we cannot decide purely on the basis of the physical events. But to give the context includes other words which are just as ambiguous, and these in their turn need to be explained, and so on and so on, so that rather than the description getting more and more accurate, it seems in a curious way to be getting looser and looser. Whatever we choose as the description of the behaviour in which we are interested, we may be confronted by people who say, "But surely you don't think that *that* is an example of someone having religious belief? What an extraordinary criterion to choose". And the conclusion begins to be forced upon us that there is no way of describing exactly how we want either the person or an artefact to behave which univocally describes "belief" behaviour. We are faced with something outside the bounds of the McCulloch-Pitts theorem.

It is almost certain that this is one of the reasons for the lack of satisfactory theories in sociology and social psychology. For one characteristic of these fields is that often, although a survey has been painstakingly done, and the data analysed with great care; or an experiment has been carefully conducted, the work provokes a response of, "It's very good, but you don't really think that what you've done is to measure X, do you?" (Where X is some aspect of human social behaviour.) Now it will be remembered that at the beginning of this chapter, we remarked on the similarity between the logical form of Turing's account of machines, and the form of scientific theories. We have shown (and we will look at further examples shortly), that certain classes of behaviour are not amenable to the description of the possibilities of Turing machines as given by McCulloch and Pitts. If we are right in saying that the form of scientific theory is identical with that of Turing machines, then it follows that any behaviour which cannot fit the definition of McCulloch and Pitts will not fit into the classical design of a scientific theory. And this is the reason for the inadequacy of the attempts to make typically social behaviour fit the model of classical scientific theory. The implications are that while much good work can be done by getting as close as possible to the rigour which the classical sciences use, there will always be the possible rejoinder "It is a very good survey/experiment, and your analysis of the data is very well done, but you don't really think that that is the criterion for a person doing X, do you?"

An example of another class of behaviour which serves to show up the looseness of the descriptions available for certain classes of behaviour is that of "loving". There is a story to the effect that a computer was once programmed to write love-letters according to the "monkeys and the typewriters" theory. That is, it had fed into it all the words which are used in love letters, and then combined them in all possible ways. Some of the letters were extremely moving and passionate. But the story concludes that the lady to whom they were sent broke off her engagement when she discovered that her fiancé was not writing them himself. What is it that makes us decide that the production of love letters is not sufficient evidence that the machine in question is in love (even with another machine!)? The same problem here arises as in the case of "belief". One of the delights of love is that there is an infinite variety in the actions which can count as the behaviour of a lover. And although we can usually recognize when people are in love by their behaviour, we cannot give a finite account of what aspects of the behaviour count as being in love un-equivocally. (If we could, then if a person wanted to know for sure whether they were in love with someone else, they could look up in a book what behaviour they ought to be showing, which suggestion is patently false.) In "loving" there is no set of events which univocally describes the behaviour involved. All sorts of things, some of them very surprising, count as loving behaviour, and it is almost impossible to imagine an action which could under no conceivable circumstance be claimed as evidence by someone that they loved another. The decision that Mr X loves Miss Y is not something which can be logically deduced from a premise, nor is it something which can be proved from empirical evidence. There is no description of Mr Y's behaviour which can be given and guarantee that we are looking at a man in love. Hence there is no possibility of giving the kind of description that is needed in order to construct an artefact to show this part of human natural history.

Another example is "thinking". But here an interesting difference arises. For there are certain kinds of thinking for which a description of the right kind can be clearly given. Generally speaking we describe an organism as thinking when it solves a problem, although in the case of trial-and-error or guessing we are rather loth to accord this description. But where a person proceeds by logical steps, as in mathematical problems, or a chess game, then we are usually inclined to say that he thought about the problem. This kind of behaviour is readily describable in terms of the behaviour which counts as solving the problem, and hence in this sense of the word "thinking" we can describe an artefact that thinks. But there are many other things which we call thinking which do not fit this pattern. Suppose that someone says that he is thinking about his summer holidays, there may be no external behaviour at all which corresponds to this; there may even be no slight muscular tensions which the Watsonians claimed were thought. And even if we record the brain patterns of the man, we merely have the same situation which arose in connection with our discussion of the criteria of "having experiences". Some forms of thinking are not univocally linked to behaviour. Here again we know that nervous activity is occurring because we know we are thinking, and not vice versa; even though there is always nervous activity present whenever we are thinking. This situation cannot be described exhaustively in terms of behaviour and therefore cannot be realized in an artefact.

Again, consider "choosing". Now it is certainly true that men, animals, and artefacts all choose in some ways. The rat in the maze selects left or right. The sheep selects one piece of grass as preferable to another. The *Machina Speculatrix* selects the light. The computer selects which circuits to activate in order to perform a particular computation. The man selects the behaviour which he considers to be good, and rejects the bad. Now all these are examples of choosing, although they differ to a greater or lesser degree. Men often choose in just the same sense as the artefacts or the animals (think of a heavy smoker "choosing" to smoke!). But he also chooses in other ways. The simple choices, left-right in a maze, tipped-or-plain-cigarette, can be described in terms of behaviour, and therefore artefacts can be made to show this sort of choice. But what about choosing the good course of action, that is, moral choice? Here again there is no behavioural description which, in a finite number of words, specifies what it is to choose the good. In fact, even more obviously than in our previous examples, what at one time would count as good may at others count as exactly the opposite depending upon the context in which the choice occurs. Hence, again, the description in terms of behaviour which we can give of moral behaviour is not of the kind which satisfies the requirements of the McCulloch and Pitts theorem, and hence such behaviour cannot be programmed for an artefact. (And this leaves aside the extra complications of a man who is pretending to be good, although his intention is really to mislead.)

Note that we have come to a conclusion about the unique quality of certain cases of human choosing without any discussion of "predictability", or "the soul", or any other such topic. The uniqueness is simply that humans show kinds of choosing which are qualitatively different, in that moral choices are not univocally describable in a finite number of words in terms of behaviour. This is the class of behaviour that is usually called "free choice". And it is worth noticing in passing that in fact such choice *is* predictable, although free, and not reducible to a behavioural account. The description of a friend in such terms as "he is a good man" is such a prediction. We do not mean simply that in the past he has always made morally good choices, but also that we are prepared to bet that when similar occasions arise in the future he will choose in the same way. It is in fact arguable that a "freely choosing" self-organizing system is *more*, not less predictable than a state-determined system. For in the latter class of system, while it is true that the outcome is completely determined by the present state of the system, there could be a very large set of possible factors which are relevant to deciding to which state of the behaviour matrix the system will move next, and we can never guarantee that we know them all. But in a "free" system, we know that most of them can be disregarded anyway. Because we know a person well, we know that however biologically seductive the girl next to him may be, he will not in fact be led astray! Although there are just as many causes which may play a part in determining the outcome, only some of them are relevant, and whatever values the others take we can ignore them. Hence a self-determining, freely choosing system is more predictable than a state-determined one in principle, once both systems become very large.

To conclude this chapter, we ought perhaps to say something about the concept of the "soul", since most Christian accounts of the nature of man make use of the concept. So far, we have been able to show that man has properties which are in principle impossible to describe in such a way that we could make an artefact (either biological—synthetic life—or electro-mechanical) which would exhibit those properties. But we have not mentioned his "soul". And indeed, within the framework of a cybernetic analysis of behaviour and experience the concept does not arise.

The soul is a concept which arises, for the scholastic philosophers, from behaviour. As Aquinas says (*Summa Theologica*, Ia, qu. 87), we can have no direct intuition or experience of the soul. We are merely conscious of our acts and experiences as our own. "The soul is what makes things alive, that is why we say that they are animate" (*Summa Theologica*, Ia, qu. 75). That is, to say a thing has a soul is to say it is a living thing. To say that different creatures have different sorts of soul is to say that they are alive in different sorts of ways, that they do different things. And traditional Christian philosophy has gone on to claim that the way in which man is alive, the things he does and the experiences he has, are such that one wants to make a very special claim about his nature. (We say that his soul is spiritual, and that it survives after death.) But notice that the way in which we decide that a particular organism is a man is by its natural history. We tell that a man has a soul by his doing those things which make us conclude that he is alive. We do not decide that he is alive by observing that he has a soul. For a soul is not the sort of thing which we can observe. The reason I know that I have a soul is not because I can be aware of it—it is not that sort of thing either —but simply that I am aware of doing things and having experiences. And since self-awareness is a matter of having experiences, and not of behaviour, then we cannot in principle programme a Turing machine to show such behaviour. The talk of man's soul, which is usually presented as if it were the first stage, and obvious way, of proving man's uniqueness, is really an analysis of the meaning of the existence of those differences between man, the other animals and artefacts, which we have been discussing in this chapter. It is a theory about why man shows these unique properties, but we do not need to call it in to show that the uniqueness exists. Our cybernetic analysis alone is enough for that, and the data which it provides are common alike to materialist and Christian. The differences just are there. Why they are there, the "meta-theory" as it were, is not, strictly speaking, within the bounds of our discussion at all, but is a matter for metaphysics.

CHAPTER VII

"THE HUMAN USE OF HUMAN BEINGS"

The title of this final chapter is taken from a book by Norbert Wiener, the father of cybernetics. In it he discussed the relation between man and man, and the relation between man and machine. He spoke of the slavery to which men had always been condemned, the tasks where the terrible drudgery and boredom tied down the human spirit in a way which was unsuited to the dignity and capacities of human nature. And he spoke of the changes which cybernetics could bring to our society if that society chose to invest in the new science rather than in weapons and the old way of life. It is a book of noble vision, and of a great humanity, and it is only fitting that we should finish our consideration of cybernetics with a reflection upon the wider implications of the subject, to which Wiener drew attention.

We have seen that the science of cybernetics offers a possible technology the like of which has never been seen before, and one which is qualitatively different from the machine age which came into being at the industrial revolution. The new machine age, the Age of the Artefact, could bring with it immense blessings. It could release men from many of the tasks which bow down and even break the human spirit. But in so doing society will be changed immensely, and we have seen that in a self-organizing system the effects of changes in desirable aspects lead to unpredictable results in other sectors.

The machines will take over the jobs, and the era of leisure will be ushered in. But shall we have educated our children to live in such a world? How will men earn, when there are many fewer jobs, and yet enough is provided for all? What new ways of organizing society will be needed to give a meaning and a dignity to being the head of a family? Can people bear to have a life of leisure? Where will the members of the society find their purpose?

We do not have time to go into these questions, and indeed it is outside the province of this book to do so. But the cybernetic revolution is going to bring with it a host of moral and ethical decisions, political and social problems, which will have to be faced. And if the revolution comes about, it is only by preparing for it that we shall be able to use it for good. These are matters to be thought about now, for already the machines are beginning to replace men on an increasing scale, and what we have seen of automation is like a child playing with bricks compared with what, if the decisions were taken and the money provided, *could* come to pass in twenty-five years. Given peace and progress, we may have less than two generations to prepare for the changes. Already one union in America is claiming a "sabbatical year", a year's holiday with pay once in seven years, in order to keep up the labour force despite automation. It behoves us to think.

In the meantime, we draw to an end. The picture of the capabilities of artefacts, machines which learn, evolve, adapt, and reproduce themselves, may seem at first sight to be a frightening one. And it is one with which we shall have to learn to live. But at the same time, we have seen that out of the analysis which cybernetics gives of the world there emerges also a new apologia for the uniqueness of man. The way of thinking is unfamiliar as yet, and of the more traditional Christian arguments there is hardly a trace. But this has a certain advantage. For to those dedicated to the use of science not for the manufacture of methods of destruction, but for the turning of the world into a place where there will be a more "human use of human beings", it provides a common picture, which can be shared by believer and unbeliever alike, and which shows man to be unique. Whether or not the philosopher or scientist goes on to conclude that man is or is not spiritual in his nature, to decide for or against the validity of religious belief, is another matter. For both alike man stands unique— a unique system in a universe of systems, a unique organism in a world of organisms, the ruler alike of animal and artefact,

"a little lower than the angels
Crowned with glory and honour".

SELECT BIBLIOGRAPHY

There are as yet few introductory books on Cybernetics, and most of the important work is in the form of papers in journals or symposia. The following have been chosen as suitable for providing a good introduction to the subject:

ASHBY, W. R.: *Design for a Brain*, London, Chapman and Hall, and New York, Wiley, 1952; *An Introduction to Cybernetics*, London, Chapman and Hall, and New York, Wiley, 1956.

GEACH, P.: *Mental Acts: Their Contents and Their Objects*, London, Routledge, and New York, Humanities Press, 1957.

HOOK, S. (Editor): *Dimensions of Mind*, New York, New York Univ. Press, 1959.

NEUMANN, J. VON: "The General and Logical Theory of Automata", in *Cerebral Mechanisms in Behaviour*, edited by L. Jeffries, New York, Wiley, 1954.

PASK, G.: *An Approach to Cybernetics*, London, Hutchinson, 1956.

WIENER, N.: *Cybernetics*, 2nd edition, New York, Wiley, 1961; *Human Use of Human Beings*, 2nd revised edition, New York, Doubleday, 1954.

WINCH, P.: *The Idea of a Social Science*, London, Routledge, 1958.

The Twentieth Century Encyclopedia of Catholicism

The number of each volume indicates its place in the over-all series and not the order of publication.

TWENTIETH CENTURY ENCYCLOPEDIA OF CATHOLICISM

All titles are subject to change.

2007

INVENTORY '80